Bunkhouse Papers

BOOKS BY

John Upton Terrell

Bunkhouse Papers   The Navajo
An American Indian Almanac of Prehistoric Times
The Man Who Rediscovered America   Traders of the Western Morning
Journey Into Darkness
The Six Turnings   La Salle
Black Robe
Zebulon Pike   Furs By Astor
Estevanico the Black
War for the Colorado River   Faint the Trumpet Sounds
Pueblo de los Corazones
Plume Rouge   Sunday Is the Day You Rest
Adam Cargo
The Little Dark Man   Apache Chronicle (1972)
Kingdom on Earth (In preparation)

FOR YOUNGER READERS

Search for the Seven Cities   The Discovery of California
The Key to Washington
United States Government Departments:
State, Treasury, Justice, Agriculture, Interior, Defense,
Post Office, Commerce, Labor, and
Health, Education, and Welfare (Ten volumes)

John Upton Terrell

Bunkhouse Papers

ILLUSTRATED BY LORENCE BJORKLUND

The Dial Press • New York, 1971

818.5
T

Foreword

ON AN EARLY SPRING DAY IN 1911, a rather scrawny boy from Chicago lost his British cap from the open observation platform as the California Limited passed through Apache Canyon in New Mexico.

It was a cap with long earflaps which could be tied together on the top of his head when not needed for protection against inclement weather. His grandmother had sent it to him from Canterbury for his tenth birthday.

That the recollection of such an insignificant misfortune would remain so vivid in my memory after the passage of half a century may be explained, I think, only by its association with an event of great importance in my life.

The incident occurred on my first trip to the West. I doubt that I have forgotten very many details of that memorable journey.

The April afternoon was bright, hot and dusty. Only the brakeman was on the platform with me at the time. We both watched the cap rise on a desert gust, the earflaps extended like wings. It vanished in the sagebrush.

He grinned sympathetically as he said, "Too bad."

My mother had seen the cap sail away from inside the car. She came out, and for a moment she stared back along the track in a way which made me think she was considering pulling the emergency cord to stop the train.

Presently she said, "Well, I hope some poor Apache boy finds it." Undoubtedly she had got the name of the canyon from the travel folder which she had followed closely as we progressed.

My father came out on the platform. She told him what had happened.

"Some Mexican will be wearing an English cap," he said, and he seemed to be intrigued by the thought.

As if she were stating a fact instead of asking a question, my mother said to the brakeman, "I suppose there are Apaches around here."

"Mostly Mexican," he said.

"Names are not always correctly applied to places," my father told her. "Come inside. It's dusty, and you'll both be blowing overboard next."

It was quite improper for anyone, even a boy of ten, to be bareheaded while traveling. In a tone of self-reproach, my mother said, "I should have expected something like this to happen and have packed another for him."

"Don't worry," my father said.

The train stopped for some time in Albuquerque. He hurried through a cup of tea in the Harvey House. Then he set off to see if he could get another cap for me. My mother had given him detailed instructions, as if he might have been going on a difficult mission to a strange country. She had admonished him, "Get something suitable." And she looked discouraged as she added, "I don't suppose you can in a place like this."

She and my brother, who was five, and I were waiting somewhat anxiously at the steps of our Pullman when he returned. He didn't have a cap.

"Really couldn't find the right sort," he reported, and from a paper bag he took a western-style hat with a wide brim. "Nothing but Indian curios, you know. This will have to do."

I put on the cowboy hat. It was a little bit too large, and it rested on my ears. My brother laughed, but I wasn't displeased. My mother only closed her eyes, as if giving up to the indefeasible power of fate.

"All aboard," the porter said.

A fortnight later, I left my glasses on a redwood stump in Muir Woods. My father and I went all the way back across San Francisco Bay from our hotel in Berkeley in an attempt to recover them. But they had disappeared.

A ranger whose aid we enlisted said they had not been turned in. My father looked deeply perturbed.

When we had returned to the hotel, he said, "This is very expensive. Not only the glasses. I suppose we'll have to stay here two or three days to get another pair. It means changing several reservations. I don't suppose he could go without them for a time?"

"Certainly not," my mother said. "He must wear them for the astigmatism in his left eye. Besides, he has his nose in a history book all the time, even when he's eating."

"Very inconvenient, really," my father said, and only then did he ask me why I had put them on the stump . . . of all places. I guess it had not occurred to him to ask the question before that.

"I know why," my brother said. "They were so dirty he

couldn't see through them to read about the big trees, and he didn't have any handkerchief to clean them."

"But I gave you a handkerchief before we left," my mother said. "I distinctly remember . . ."

"He lost it, too," my brother said.

I heard them talking about the increasing cost of the trip, and my mother reminded my father that she had suggested it be postponed for a year, but that he had been unwilling to wait.

"Well, I haven't changed my mind," he said. "Boys should travel as young as possible. As soon as they can appreciate things. We'll make out. I want them to see the West."

Whenever he said *the West* there was a kind of reverence in his voice. It was as if he were speaking of something for which he held a great affection and a profound respect. But I would come to know in time that, more than affection or respect, his feeling was one of mingled admiration and wonder, admiration for the beauty and wonder at the immensity. For the same emotion would live in me.

I would know other emotions my father never experienced. There was a pronounced difference in our natures and in our reactions and in our way of thinking. He had the ability to shut out ugliness he did not wish to see. I did not. He could ignore reality. I could not. He could project himself into a pleasant world of his own creation. But the history I studied and absorbed, and which so greatly fascinated me, would not let me retreat into fancies and shut the door to the truth.

We went on to the Yellowstone National Park from California. My mother wanted me to discard the cowboy hat for a proper cap she had obtained for me in San Francisco, but I persuaded her to let me keep it. Through the weeks it stretched and rode my ears. My new glasses seemed to have a similar weakness. They slipped down my nose.

However, I was concerned little about my personal appearance, especially when I sat beside the driver of the big four-horse carry-all on the drive through the Yellowstone.

It was at that time a sensation returned which I had first experienced at the Grand Canyon.

We had spent a night and a day at the canyon. In the afternoon we had walked along the rim from the El Tovar Hotel. The altitude had bothered my mother, and she had turned back, taking my brother with her.

My father and I had descended the Bright Angel Trail for perhaps half a mile. The sights and sounds of the inhabited world above were obliterated. It would not have been difficult to believe that they no longer existed anywhere under the sky. There remained only space and silence, unimaginable space, unbelievable silence.

We sat on a rock and stared into the magnificent depths. There the strange sensation came to me. It stirred in me a kind of apprehension I had never known, a fearful impression that I had become a prisoner of forces too powerful to be overcome, indeed, forces so great that any defiance would have been futile.

"It's all too much," I said. "Let's go back."

My father stared curiously at me. Then he followed me up the trail without speaking.

As I watched the blue-green forests sweeping against the peaks of the Yellowstone, as I gazed into distance that hour after hour became more inconceivable, the mysterious sensation returned. I knew again the apprehension. But now it was followed by an inexplicable thought: that it was a reaction which in some way would influence my life, and that I would know it many times.

I have never subscribed to the contention that emotions are exclusively the products of time lived, of experience or intellectual development. For they are inherent, born when one is born, reflections from one's own nature.

Nor have I ever believed that the very young have no great moments. For they do have them . . . moments that all the pain of knowledge and all the burdens of understanding acquired in a lifetime may not relegate to oblivion.

Retrospection long ago made it clear that I felt the weight of a transcending emotion in the tenth year of my life. If I could not understand it then, I sensed its significance.

I knew, as I went home from that first journey to the West, that I would go back.

And I did go back . . . even sooner than I might have expected.

Less than six years later, when I was still sixteen, I watched the ranges of Montana, shimmering in the bright green of early summer, unfold from the door of an empty boxcar.

Bunkhouse Papers

1

<hr />

I DON'T BELIEVE a man ever forgets a bunkhouse in which he lived long enough to learn something of the other occupants.

For a bunkhouse . . . at least, it was true in the years of my early western wanderings . . . stood apart as an institution. It was an exception to every commonplace standard to which the general society adhered and sought to maintain. It represented a distinct and unique phase of American culture. If it were restricted to the West, if it were regional, its significance in the scheme of national life was in no way diminished.

For the bunkhouse stood prominently in the foreground of every type of western representation. No account of the customs, no study, no dissertation, no fiction . . . indeed, no history . . . could be complete and authentic without recognition of its influence, without consideration of the effects it had on the behavior and the minds of all persons, young and old, who dwelt in an immense region that embraced the larger part of the United States.

The bunkhouse was not only a home, not only a shelter, not only a depository for possessions.

The bunkhouse was also a forum.

It was a fountain of ideas, of beliefs, of conceptions. It was a news agency. And it was a harbor for dreams.

In it one heard vulgarities of every conceivable kind.

In it one heard stories of great drama, tragedies and comedies, stories of revolting degeneracy and of transcending beauty.

The economy of almost every western area stemmed in a major part from the men who lived in its bunkhouses. For these were the men who worked in the fields, who rode the ranges, who husbanded the cattle and the sheep, who pitted themselves against the dust storms and the heat and the blizzards and the droughts, the men who spent their wages in the local saloons and stores and whorehouses, the men who branded and shipped and lambed and castrated and planted and harvested.

There would have been small progress and little development and a crippled economy without them. They were the producers.

Almost all of them lived under conditions which, if not as bad as those to be found in some city tenements, were comparable to the crudeness and the squalor of a sod shanty or the dilapidation and raggedness of the little shacks that fringe western towns.

With a single exception, every bunkhouse I knew in Montana, in Wyoming, in Colorado, in Idaho, in Arizona, in New Mexico, had the aspect of a badger hole and the atmosphere of a pig wallow.

Some of them were built of logs, and some of clapboard, and some were an incongruous combination of several ma-

The bunkhouse was not only a home, not only a shelter, not only a depository for possessions. The bunkhouse was also a forum.

terials, a patchwork of stone and adobe and tin and wood. Some had roofs of iron sheeting which made them unbearably hot in summer and unbearably cold in winter. Some had dirt floors.

And none of them . . . with that single exception . . . had plumbing of any kind, neither tubs nor showers nor toilets.

There was always an adjacent backhouse, but most of them were undesirable, even for their intended function. The stench usually was overwhelming. In warm months clouds of flies made it virtually impossible to remain in them long enough to complete successfully, and certainly not peacefully, the mission in mind.

Most men . . . and few ranch workers could be accused of excessive fastidiousness . . . preferred to retreat to the corrals or the manure piles behind the stables or a creek or a grove of trees, if one of these sanctuaries were reasonably close, to answer the calls of nature. Rain and hot sun and natural disintegrative processes in these exposed places performed to some extent the sanitary measures that owners and operators of ranches did not trouble to undertake.

Beside every bunkhouse stove was a box of sand. It was designed to receive expectorations, either natural salivary secretions or those compounded with tobacco or snuff juices. On cold or rainy nights the sandbox also was handy as a urinal. Anyone who has smelled the odor of spatters of urine sizzling on a hot stove would never forget it.

Some bunkhouses had wooden bunks built in tiers. No mattresses. Some had iron cots, or an assortment of cots and single bedsteads. No mattresses. However, the absence of these commonplace household appurtenances of comfort was unquestionably advantageous to all concerned. For they would have remained in the condition each user left them, retain-

7

ing the respective scents, if not the crawling and jumping parasites, of unwashed men.

On some ranches, a chicken wrangler or handyman, generally old or crippled hands no longer able to perform ordinary duties, occasionally swept the bunkhouse floor. The usual method was to sprinkle water here and there. This system not only failed to settle dust, but it created cakes of mud under beds, in corners, and about the legs of any chairs that might happen to be among the accouterments. However, chairs were seldom to be enountered in bunkhouses. There were corners, of course, but in most bunkhouses their angles were made invisible by mounds of hardened dirt, discarded clothing, and other debris.

Invariably safeguards were established to prevent the entrance of fresh air. Windows were seldom opened, even if it were possible to disengage them from their accumulations of sediment. Rags and pieces of cardboard and newspapers and flattened cans blocked drafts from cracks or supplanted broken panes. Doors were always closed at night. A supply of oxygen that was no more than barely adequate to begin with was quickly exhausted in the early night hours. And one's throat was dried and one's nostrils assailed by an atmospheric prescription derived from stale cigarette butts, sweat, spit, and noisome exhalations.

No doubt long before my time in the West . . . and perhaps it is still true . . . almost every habitué of a western bunkhouse had to be a linguist of modest attainments. He was required to speak, or at least to understand, no less than two tongues. If he did not possess this ability he could not make himself clearly understood, nor could he grasp the full meaning of the conversations he heard.

One of these tongues might be called a *special* language, and the other a *public* language.

The first was somewhat restricted in its use. For, although

8

it might have been understood, it most assuredly would have been unappreciated and misinterpreted beyond the confines of a corral, a cow camp, an irrigated field, and, of course, the bunkhouse itself.

The second had a wider range of usage. It was generally acceptable in such places as stores, cafés, hotels, on railroad trains and stages, and in the offices of lawyers and doctors. Another place in which it could be spoken without undue hazard was in the home of relatives who resided in a town and among whom were women of more refinement than might be exhibited in the parlor of a brothel.

Of the two languages, that normally heard in a bunkhouse was, I have always been convinced, one of the most remarkable on earth. My reasoning in this analysis was not based on its peculiar grammatical construction nor on its complexities. For it had no rules of grammar. And it was incomparably simple.

Besides the necessary proper nouns, and a sprinkling of prepositions, it had only six basic words. They were shit, fuck, piss, fart, cock, and asshole.

The thoughts which could be expressed, the messages which could be conveyed to listeners, the tales which could be told, and the information which could be disseminated with those six words were no less than utterly astounding. They served as nouns, verbs, adverbs, adjectives and participles—past and present, if not future.

One might easily have been misled into believing that it was a language not difficult to learn or which one might, after slight practice, speak with fluency. That would have been a gross misapprehension, a serious mistake.

It would have been unwise for anyone . . . and I could so testify as a result of my own experience . . . to have attempted its employment without long exposure to it. For not only were intense training and actual practice required before one could speak it properly, not to mention understand it, but one's ears had to be well attuned to its peculiar inflections and many tonal qualities.

Moreover, the accompaniment of certain definite gestures was mandatory. It had an undeniable, if somewhat vague, affiliation with the sign language.

But the bunkhouse was, after all, security. It was a relatively safe den.

And by its very nature it held open the door to freedom. It was not a prison. A man could always move on . . . on to another bunkhouse.

2

I REACHED THE BUNKHOUSE COUNTRY after an un-
planned and unpleasant period of servitude in Kansas.
But it might be said that my western migration really
began in 1917 on a cold gray February day when two men
from the United States Department of Agriculture appeared
at Chicago's Nicholas Senn High School.

The men had been expected, at least by the principal,
and he had instructed all the teachers to have the largest and
strongest male students report to the main auditorium at two
o'clock. Perhaps he had included in his message the qualifica-
tion *dumbest*. For I observed that among the group were the
outstanding numbskulls and blockheads of the school. Each
of them displayed a physique that would have made a foot-
ball coach rub his hands in eager anticipation.

My imagination had been stimulated by the order to
proceed to the auditorium. As I walked along the corridor, I
wondered if there was to be an invasion by the Germans, and

if we were to be called upon to defend our homes and our city, as in the past men had been summoned to repel an Indian attack. Admittedly it did not take much in the way of interruptions of academic routine to stir excitement in me, but I felt that in this case my fears were justifiable. U-boats were sinking our ships. The war was going badly for the Allies. One had no way of knowing what to expect.

The principal, Benjamin Buck, was speaking when I got to the auditorium. He was telling the youths before him that they represented the school's "finest, if not always the best in grades, certainly the best in physical ability."

It was his kind of humor. He smiled weakly, as if his own words made him nervous, but he frowned as he said, "In this situation, studies must be subordinated to muscular power . . . I fear."

Then he quickly added, "The combination of brains and brawn, however, is always desirable."

It was not disclosed that the Kaiser had formulated plans to invade the United States, but the assembly did have to do with the war. Mr. Buck said, "We have not felt it directly . . . that is, most of us . . . but I fear the time has come."

I had the feeling that he was saddened by the thought of the boys who had gone, who had enlisted. That would have been out of the question for me. For I had broken my left arm playing basketball at the Y.M.C.A., and although I had full use of it, the elbow was slightly crooked. Besides, there was the astigmatism which forced me to wear glasses.

The principal went on: "The country, as you no doubt have read or heard, is faced with a serious and growing shortage of manpower on our farms. The Government has requested all Boards of Education to cooperate with it in alleviating this shortage."

The older and stronger students (male) would be asked to volunteer to fill the gaps made by farm workers who had

12

gone into war plants and into service. The two men from the United States Department of Agriculture had come to tell us of the new organization called the Working Reserve Bureau.

"But if you volunteer, you will suffer no loss of credits," he said. His face was sorrowful, and he seemed to choke a bit. "I know some of you are seniors who would graduate in June. But let me assure you that you will graduate, even if you are not here . . . under these unavoidable circumstances."

I thought: Plowing, you pass history. Haying, you get an A in geometry. Riding a corn planter, you receive a diploma.

The Working Reserve Bureau was in a newly partitioned basement of an old building in the Loop.

It was crowded with youths from all sections of Chicago. As I waited in the line to which a guard had directed me, I had the thought that only the red, white and blue file cards being used by the men and women at the row of desks preserved a semblance of order under conditions which might easily have become chaotic.

In my hand I held the letter the principal had given me. Presently a man took it. "Desk Number Twenty," he commanded. "Move up, move up, everybody keep moving up, please!"

Desk Number Twenty was littered with papers. The man sitting at it was bald, he fidgeted in his chair, and he had a habit of stroking an eyebrow with the eraser of a pencil.

"Sit there," he said, pointing to a straight chair at one end of the desk. "Give me your identification. Now, first your description. Tall for your age, eh? Blue eyes. Complexion fair. Any scars?"

"Appendicitis."

He nodded in a way that made me think he had expected the answer. "Religion?"

13

When I did not reply at once, he glanced sharply at me. "Church, church, what church?" He poised his pen. "What's the matter? Don't you know your church?"

"I was wondering what that had to do with going to work on a farm," I said.

"Well, stop wondering," he said in a tone of hopelessness. "I don't think that's any of your business, anyway. The Government wants certain questions answered. What's your religion?"

"I don't think that's any of the Government's business," I said.

He leaned back. I wasn't certain whether he was amused or annoyed when he asked: "You want to work on a farm, don't you?"

"Not especially," I said, "but I've volunteered to do it."

He took a deep breath. Then he wrote something on a white card. I thought he wrote the words *No Church,* but looking at them upside down I could not be certain.

I told him, "I was hoping to be sent out West. To Montana or Wyoming or maybe to California."

For the first time he smiled, and he said, "I'd like to go to one of those places for the summer, too. However, it happens that you're going to Kansas. Get your letter of introduction at Desk Number Forty." He dismissed me with a slight gesture, as if he might have been brushing a fly from his coat. "Next, please," he called out.

I left him with the feeling that he was happy in the knowledge that he had prevented me from going to the places for which I had expressed a preference.

It was almost full spring in southern Kansas. The local train on that Sunday morning consisted of an engine, a baggage car, and a day coach.

"Round Point! Next stop! Round Point!" the conductor

14

The short main street of Round Point ran away at an angle from the depot. I could see no one on it.

shouted, as if he were trying to make seven deaf passengers understand that a momentous event was about to occur.

A woman and two little girls got off with me. The woman wore a severely cut dark suit which looked as if it might once have been a uniform from which brass buttons had been removed. A small elderly man in overalls was at the depot to meet them. He put his arms around each of the little girls and kissed them. Then he shook hands with the woman. Then he put his arms around the little girls again, and I thought he was crying. At last he took up their suitcases. They drove away. I wondered who the woman was and why he had not kissed her.

A small blackboard had columns headed *TO* and *FROM,* but no train schedules were chalked on it. Across the single track was a plowed field, its even furrows sharply black against a woods in which new leaves glistened brightly green in brilliant sunlight. Only the clicking of the telegraph key broke the silence.

The short main street of Round Point ran away at an angle from the depot. I could see no one on it. As I was moving my valise into the shade, a Ford sedan came around a corner. It moved slowly, almost hesitantly, up to the platform. Although its engine had died with a cough, the man driving continued to sit with his hands on the wheel. He stared at me, but his expression gave no indication of his thoughts.

"Mr. Kunze?" I said.

He nodded and got out. He was tall and bony, his shoulders wide and sharp, and big hands dangled out of the sleeves of a black suit which hung loosely about him. A brown fedora sat very straight and very high on his head. His brown shoes had what were popularly called bulldog toes. Metal spectacles rode the high bridge of a thin nose, and small black eyes peered suspiciously through them.

"You ain't waited long," he said, as if he were expecting

me to complain. "I left when I seen the train come by. These trains shouldn't be allowed to run on a Sunday, and . . ."

He stopped as I drew from my pocket the letter of introduction with which the Bureau had provided me. I had read it, for it had not been sealed. It avowed that I was a patriotic and industrious young man. Following that accolade, it directed Frank Kunze to fill out the enclosed card and return it to the Bureau. No postage was required. The penalty for private use was $300.

He nodded as he read the letter, as if keeping time with his head. Then he said, "You missed church this morning."

That, I thought, was rather obvious. Church services weren't usually held on local trains running through Kansas cornfields. I made no reply.

"If you had come yesterday," he said, "you could have went with us this morning. Put your bag in the back."

We drove along a street that was lined with neat white frame houses, all of which seemed to be built in the shape of an ell. There were fine big trees around most of them, and some of the yards were enclosed by white picket fences.

I remarked that it was pleasant weather.

He said, "Too hot. But it won't last. We'll have some cold days yet. It's not good to get so hot this early. Things start too fast." As if he were stating an irrefutable fact, he said, "You never worked on a farm."

"I've spent several summers on them. Vacations."

"But never worked."

"I've driven a haying team, and I've cultivated corn."

"But not work."

We passed the last house of the town and crossed a brook. The fields began, sweeping away from each side of the road without interruption, except by a few small islands of trees.

"You can't harness a team."

"I've helped to do it."

20

"But you don't know how."

"I guess not."

He drove with maddening slowness. Several times the engine almost died for lack of fuel. He sat up very straight in his seat, his arms straight out to the top of the wheel. The car wandered.

"Twenty dollars a month and board for a boy that can't do nothing seems like a lot."

I didn't look at him, and I remained silent, and I felt warmth in my cheeks.

"I guess in wartime we can't complain too much," he said. "We have to put up with things and make some sacrifices."

Some people do, I thought. But I said nothing.

We passed two men who were harrowing, and he waved laconically at them, and said, "On my place, we don't work on Sunday. They're Catholics."

The land was slightly rolling, but the rises were not great enough to prevent cultivation. We passed a large house set in a grove of trees, and I remarked that it was an attractive place.

He sniffed and said, "That shows you don't know nothing about farmin'. You won't find no trees takin' up any of my land that can be used. No hedgerows, neither."

He made a bad turn from the highway into a rutted dirt road, and brought the car back to an even keel in the manner of one attempting to right a boat. A bunting shot like a blue arrow over the hood and vanished in some lettuce-green willows. I heard a lark sing, and somewhere in the distance a cow bawled.

But there *were* some trees on his farm. There were several poplars standing along the lane that led to the small frame house . . . also built in the shape of an ell . . . which was badly in need of paint. A low board fence, which had never known paint, enclosed a little dooryard in which there were two barren flower beds encircled by whitewashed stones.

A hard-packed soil area stretched away to a large barn. Beyond the barn I could see a number of pig sties. A partly dismantled tractor stood before an open implement shed. Some geese waddled in a military maneuver toward a small pond behind a dripping watering trough.

As we came in our wandering fashion up the lane a girl who was sitting in a rocking chair on the small porch got up and went into the house. I was taking my valise from the car when a woman and a small child appeared at the screened door.

"The new boy," Frank Kunze said.

"How do you do," I said, but she only nodded, and the slight smile which flickered across her thin lips disclosed gaps where teeth were missing. Her dark eyes were not unfriendly, but they seemed to be too large for her small face, and I had the impression she had borrowed them from some larger woman, perhaps to wear on Sunday. She did not offer to open the door. I dropped my valise on the porch, and we all stood in an awkward silence.

At last Frank Kunze said, "Show him his place."

Two small girls were standing just inside a parlor that opened off the large kitchen. One of them suddenly covered her face with an apron and turned away. The other stared at me. The older girl, who had been sitting on the porch, was working at a sink which had a hand pump at one end. She did not turn to look at me.

"It's up them stairs," Mrs. Kunze said. "The room on the right."

I thanked her and started up. The stairs were so narrow that I was obliged to hold my valise ahead of me to climb them. The door of the room creaked as I pushed it open. I stood on the threshold looking at a wooden bed that was covered with a patchwork quilt.

The bed took up most of the floor space, with only a

narrow passage between it and a small chest of drawers. There was no carpet on the wide uneven boards of the floor. On the chest was a glass kerosene lamp, but it had no chimney. In one corner was a washstand with a bowl and pitcher on it, but the pitcher contained no water. The towel which hung on a wall rack obviously had been used.

The air seemed stale and dank, as if the room had been closed for some time. I opened the small window. The view was of the barnyard.

A wave of loneliness swept through me, and I felt a strange feeling of nausea, but these sensations were quickly supplanted by anger. I knew a strong impulse to turn back down the stairs.

I dropped down on the bed. And I felt like crying. And perhaps I did . . . a little.

During the first week we worked at disking and harrowing. Frank Kunze let me know each day how dissatisfied he was with my performance. He complained that I didn't know how to drive a team straight, and I walked too slowly, and I didn't seem to be interested in doing a good job. The fact that I did not know how to operate a cream separator seemed to astonish him.

He included the federal government in his criticisms: "They shouldn't take no good men in the Army who was raised on farms. They could get enough in the cities. But they want only the best, I guess. Only they should leave us enough to do the work right."

I was bone-tired each day, and his derogations only increased my weariness. Once I retorted angrily, "I do as well as I can. You ought to take into consideration that I wasn't raised on a farm."

"You don't need to tell me that," he said. "But I think I can learn you."

Nora Kunze and Frank and Nora's niece, Mary Hewitt,

23

did the milking in the morning and in the evening. I fed and bedded down the horses in the stable, and then I turned the separator. Darkness had fallen each evening before we had got the cans of milk and cream ready to be picked up by the truck from the Round Point Creamery. I was sick from hunger before we sat down for supper.

Each meal was a swilling match. The children ate with the efficiency and manner of pigs. Frank and Nora were the hog callers. There was little said at the table. Frank seemed to think that talking while eating was an unnecessary exercise. If one of the children started to speak, he would grunt, "Eat your food."

Katherine was eight, a year older than Little Nora, and at times her mouth hung open, as if she were having difficulty breathing. I guess she was, for she wasn't an idiot. Little Nora had the straight black hair and immense black eyes of her mother, but Katherine's hair was brown, and she was a rather pretty girl, but her prettiness was marred by her squinting. I thought she was badly in need of glasses. Little Frank's hair was the color of corn, and his eyes were round and brightly blue and set widely apart. He was too fat, and he was greasy, as if he not only ate too much pork but anointed himself with it. At times Little Frank made sucking noises, and Frank would growl at him to stop. If he repeated the noises, Frank would raise a hand, as if he were going to strike him. He didn't strike him, but Little Frank would appear to be terrified, and he would spew half-chewed food over himself and the tray of his high chair.

Dishes were not passed. Before I was aware of this inviolable understanding, I asked if I might have a piece of bread, which was on the opposite side of the table. Nora seemed embarrassed and dropped her eyes as she handed me the bread plate. Always after that I reached for the food I wanted, even

24

though I had to raise a bit from my chair to complete the operation.

"Don't put butter and jam on your bread at the same time," Frank Kunze said. "Use one or the other."

Nora, too, seemed perturbed by my infraction of the rule. She said, "I expect city people are used to wasting things."

"We have to work here for what we get," Frank said. "You seem to eat mighty big for such a thin boy."

I made sure that I had eaten everything on my plate, then followed their custom of wiping it with a piece of bread. One evening as I left the table, I saw that Mary Hewitt was watching me. I had the feeling she was trying to tell me something with her eyes, something consoling or kind, and I felt a little better as I went up to my room.

Each night I fell across the bed, too tired to begin undressing at once, and I told myself I didn't care what they said.

I had some difficulty finding words which described Mary Hewitt's hair and eyes to my satisfaction, but one day when it was raining and I had been put to oiling harness I met with some success.

She had been gathering eggs, and she came into the little room at the end of the barn where I was working, and she sat for a time on an old broken chair.

That was the first occasion on which she disclosed anything about herself. I had the impression that she wanted to do it, but perhaps she would have been glad of an opportunity to talk with anyone who would be interested in hearing what she had to say. On the farm, at least, I was the only one who did not display reluctance in that respect.

She was fifteen, and she was the daughter of Nora Kunze's sister, and she had lived there almost two years. Her father was a railroad engineer. He paid the Kunzes for boarding her, but she more than earned the money by the work she did. When her mother died, her father had sold his house in Topeka. He had promised to take her back there to live in an apartment in the fall, and she was counting off the days· on a little calendar which she kept among the cobwebs of a cupboard in the harness room.

I rejected *rust* and settled on *sherry.* For her hair reminded me of the wine my father prized so greatly and which he kept in a cut-glass decanter on the sideboard of our dining room.

"You aren't going to stay long, are you?" she said, as if the question were already answered in her own mind.

I decided that *misty turquoise* wasn't quite right for her eyes, but I accepted it.

"You can confide in me," she said. "I don't like it here, either."

"Probably not," I said.

"The war does peculiar things."

"I don't think they know much about it here."

"Oh, some people do," she said. "The Masters do. They live on the second farm toward town. Paul Kincaid was their son-in-law. He was a Coast Guard officer, and he was killed at sea. They brought the two little girls back here. Their daughter committed suicide after Paul was killed."

"Two little girls . . ."

"Did you know them?" she said with surprise.

"No, but they got off the train with me."

"They said Sheilah Masters fell out a window, but we heard that she lost her mind when he was killed. What are you looking at?"

"Your hair," I said. "It's very beautiful."

And then the misty turquoise was supplanted by a brittle blue. "Once I went to Chicago with Daddy. He got a pass. He took me to the Art Institute. Did you ever go there?"

26

"Often."

"That's where I'd like to study." She gazed wistfully at the wall. "Uncle Frank and Aunt Nora think I'm silly. I mean, wanting to study painting."

"They would. Do you paint now?"

"At school . . . when I can. Uncle Frank scolded me for wasting my time."

"How would he know?"

She laughed. "But Daddy doesn't think so. He's going to let me go to art school this fall."

"I'd like to see what you paint."

"Really!" And then she saddened. "They're not much, I guess. We don't have a real art teacher here, but they let me paint an hour a day. A boy paints with me."

She seemed to be looking far beyond me, and I had the feeling that she was seeing herself walking into the Art Institute, up the wide steps from Michigan Avenue, between the great lions, and through the towering doors. Suddenly she said, almost angrily, "I know one thing. I'm not going to get stuck here, and have to get married and live in a place like this . . . not like they live."

"I'll write you when I go back to Chicago."

"You better not. Uncle Frank opens my letters. Or Nora does."

Damn them! I thought. "They shouldn't . . ."

"Even the ones I get from Daddy."

"You're too intelligent and beautiful to live here," I said, and I wondered if the boy with whom she painted an hour each day felt that way about her.

There was the brittle blue again. It was like a warning, and it gave me a slight chill. "I'll write you anyway. And maybe I'll see you . . ." I said.

She got up. And she smiled. And the misty turquoise

returned. "Maybe," she said. And she took up her basket of eggs and went out.

On the first Sunday I was there, Frank Kunze had told me that we would leave to go to church at ten o'clock. He had ordered me to wear my "good suit." I had obeyed.

Katherine complained of a stomach ache, and she was left at home with Little Frank. Nora and Frank sat in the front seat of the car, and Mary Hewitt and Little Nora and I sat in the back.

As we came into Round Point, Mary Hewitt pointed out her school.

"We have good schools here," Frank said. "I guess you have a lot of graft and stealin' and things in the Chicago schools."

I told him I was not informed on the matter.

"I read somewhere they was pretty bad," he said. "There were . . . some things going on. It said boys kept liquor in their lockers. And some other things went on."

"I suppose you have Jews, too," Nora said.

"I guess we have about every nationality," I said. "My own school has more than three thousand students."

Frank glanced suspiciously at me. "That's more people than live in Round Point."

"Jews!" Nora said, as if she were going to be sick. "That must be awful."

"They got a lot o' niggers, too," Frank said.

And she clicked her tongue several times.

"We don't have many around here," Frank said, "but there's some Dagos work on the railroad section."

"There are Jewish people in Topeka," Mary said, "and Daddy thinks they are as nice as anybody."

"Well, your father always did have some queer notions," Nora said. "They ought to make both Jews and niggers keep

28

to themselves. I've heard tell every one of them has some bad sickness."

"But I simply don't think that's true. Daddy said . . .."

"That's enough," Frank said.

The church was a tall narrow brick structure. There were a number of cars and several wagons in the yard beside it. As we went in, I knew once more the strong impulse to bolt and run, run all the way to the depot and take the first train that came along.

When we came out after the service, Frank stopped to talk with some men in the churchyard, and we waited in the car for him.

Nora said in a cold flat tone, "Have you always lived in Chicago?"

"Yes," I said.

She shook her head, as if she felt sorry for me.

"I liked Chicago," Mary said. "The lake . . . and Daddy took me to the livestock show."

"That's a wonderful thing to see," I said. "I've gone several times."

"Why?" Nora asked. "Your people ain't farmers." Her voice was antagonistic. "I guess them city people go to see all them fancy ridin' horses and men and women in tight britches. I don't know what good horses like them could be to anybody."

"We rode on the Elevated," Mary said.

Little Nora said, "We got the best horses in the world, ain't we, Ma? An' the best pigs, an' the best cows, an' . . .."

"Shut up," Nora said.

"I'd love to go again," Mary said.

Nora grunted. "What you'd like is to take it easy like city people. Maybe just sit and draw pitchers."

Frank got in the car, and no one spoke until we were almost back to the farm. Then he said: "You don't seem to care much about church. You wasn't payin' no attention to the sermon. It seems that some folks are mighty careless about the way they bring up their kids."

I said nothing, but I wanted to strike him in the face. When we reached the house, I went at once to my room, and I sat on the edge of the bed, staring out at the barnyard.

After a few minutes my anger began to subside, but I was still filled with a feeling of helplessness and disconsolation. An immediate departure would have solved the situation, but complications would have remained. I wondered if the Working Reserve Bureau would understand, and would send me some other place. I wondered if the man at Desk Number Twenty would believe me. I wished I could have talked with my father. I sat there quiet and motionless, but I was torn and confused by the questions and the arguments and the doubts and fears which seethed in me.

I was never to know what brought the decision to stay there until the first month had passed. I was never to identify the reasoning . . . if it can be called that . . . from which it derived. Perhaps it was emotion, emotion generated by a combination of stubbornness and fear.

I would know, however, an almost overwhelming loneliness.

The big horses got to know me. I thought they liked me, and that was a good feeling. The gray gelding would rub his nose against my shoulder when I went in his stall, and the black with the two white stockings and the strange cluster of lumps on her neck would nicker to me. Once when I rubbed the nose of the dappled Percheron as it stood at the pasture fence, it humped its back and bounded off, frightening itself with a series of posterior detonations.

As I harnessed the two coffee-brown mares one morning, Frank said, "We'll haul manure today. Hitch up to the spreader."

"There's something I want to tell you," I said.

He squinted at me. "What?" he said.

"My month will be up tomorrow, and I've decided to leave," I said.

He leaned against the stall and looked down his nose, as if he were trying to see beyond it. "Well, what for?" he said. Then he turned away without waiting for an answer.

I hitched the team to the spreader and drove it to the manure pile behind the barn.

"I was just thinkin'," he said. "Next week we might get some time to go fishin'."

It was difficult for me to speak with the calmness I desired. "I've decided to go."

"I guess you think you have to work too hard."

"That's not the only reason."

He began to pitch manure into the spreader. "We can work as we talk. I guess Mary was goin' to ask you to the school dance next week."

That, I knew, was not the truth. She had spoken to me about the dance, and she had said she was going with the boy who was her painting companion. And I had wondered if they would be alone together.

"Well, I wouldn't object to puttin' five dollars to your wages," Frank said. "It would be too bad if I had to tell the govermint you didn't want to work an' help in the war. So, I guess you better change your mind."

I felt an urge to hit him with the pitchfork. My fingers tightened on the handle, but I threw a forkful of manure into the spreader with force. And I said, "There's something you should know. It's about church."

He stopped working and stared at me. "What about church?"

"I'm not a Lutheran. I'm not a Protestant, as you think. I'm a Catholic."

Instantly I was angry at myself. I had not planned to lie. It came without any premeditation. It simply crossed my lips.

He stuck his pitchfork into the manure. "You deceived me."

"No, I didn't," I said. "I never told you I belonged to any church. And I don't care what church people go to."

His lips twisted, as if fury pressed against them. I thought he was going to strike me, and I stepped back, but the coldness that had come into his eyes melted. "Well, I might even forget that," he said, "as long as you go regular with us."

"I don't want to," I said.

Then he shouted: "All right! You can get your things right now. I'll take you to town. You're fired!" He threw down his pitchfork. "The govermint people will hear from me. I told 'em I didn't want nobody but a good Protestant boy. Go on!"

I went to my room to pack my valise. Then I discovered that letters I had received from my mother and father apparently had been read by someone else. They were disarranged in the drawer of the chest, and a page of one had been left out of an envelope.

I stood in the doorway of my room trembling and sickened by my resentment.

He was waiting with some money in his hand when I came out of the house with my bag. He give me nineteen dollars.

"I thought I was to get twenty," I said.

"You backed over that gas can the other day with the tractor."

"You said it was an old can and no good."

"Well, I figger it was worth a dollar to me." He turned toward the car. "Get in. I can't waste all day takin' you to town."

Once, as we drove along the lane, I looked back. The

only person I saw was Mary Hewitt. She was standing in the door of the barn with her egg basket. And she was watching us.

Frank stopped the car on the main street, and he said, "You can get out here."

He drove on without further word. The car made a bad turn as it wandered from sight around a corner.

At the depot I learned that I would have to wait nearly six hours for the next train to Kansas City. I sat disconsolately on a crate.

Then I saw that a freight train stood on a siding a short distance down the track, and as if I were impelled by actions over which I had no control, I took up my bag and walked toward it. In the same manner, without hesitation or consideration, I climbed into an empty box car.

However, I did have one thought which I never forgot. It was: Plowing, I will not pass in history. Riding in a box car, I will never get an A in English.

When the express train for which the freight was waiting had passed, it began to move, crawling slowly back onto the mainline. It was not going toward Kansas City.

It was going west.

3

THE FIRST MAN I SAW, in the first bunkhouse I ever knew, was sitting naked in a washtub of blue liquid. He was soothing his piles.

It was shortly before noon on a fine May day. And the mountains were deep blue, almost the color of the liquid in the washtub. And green waves of hills rolled against them, breaking around dark islands of pines. The floor of Montana's Madison Valley reached away in immense tilted ranges into hazy distance.

We had come out from Bozeman by train and auto stage to Ennis. But we had arrived in Ennis a day sooner than we had been expected, and no one had been there to take us out to the ranch on which we were to work.

There was no place in Ennis for us to stay. But that did not matter. Any sort of lodging, even a cot, would have cost at least a dollar, and I don't believe any of the three men with whom I was traveling could have managed that much. I had only two dollars and eighty-six cents.

But we all had our own bedrolls, and we spread them under some trees and made a fire and we bought some canned meat and some bread and a can of peaches in the grocery. We were not uncomfortable, but one of the men complained because we didn't have coffee, and one said it was a drink he wanted more than coffee. I knew he needed it, for his hands shook and he looked as if he had been drunk for some time.

All three were much older than I, perhaps twice my age or more. I wouldn't be seventeen until the coming December. All three had worked on ranches for a good many years . . . when they worked.

One of them was small and had an eagle beak that looked damp on its point. One of them had a cast in his left eye. One of them, the one who wanted liquor, looked emaciated and his teeth were two rows of brown snags, and, unfortunately, he smiled whenever he spoke, giving them full exposure. I felt sorry for him and I loaned him fifteen cents so he could buy some tobacco—he had a pack of brown cigarette papers—but I was never repaid.

At a later time I would hear someone make the remark that any cross-eyed idiot son-of-a-bitch with only one leg could get a job on a ranch that year for a hundred bucks a month, and if he had two legs and knew enough to keep from pissing in his pants, he could get five bucks a day herding sheep. All ranchers were desperately in need of men. Only a glance at my companions was needed to substantiate that statement. It was given further substantiation by my own presence in Ennis. A skinny inexperienced kid from the East . . . Chicago was the East to people in Montana . . . who had never seen the inside of a bunkhouse and who had worked on a farm only a month, was hired with no questions asked.

In the morning at Ennis, I willingly depleted my financial resources to a greater extent by purchasing a small sack of coffee. We made it in a can and washed some bread down with

36

*The first man I saw, in the first bunkhouse
I ever knew, was sitting naked in a washtub
of blue liquid.*

it. Then we went to sit on the loading platform in front of the grocery like four lost pigeons.

An hour later a Model T without a top halted before us. The man who got out of it walked as if he were permanently twisted a little to his port side. He appeared to take it for granted that we were the men he had come to meet, and without speaking he indicated to us to load our bedrolls and suitcases aboard the battered car. Then, almost without pausing he went into the store.

When he emerged he carried two large sacks of groceries. These he unceremoniously deposited on top of us. Then he cranked the Model T, which began to move forward at once with the revival of its energy. He jumped into the driver's seat, and all five of us, a jumble of sacks and bedrolls and suitcases and bodies, rolled with swiftly increasing speed only a wheel turn ahead of a cornucopia of dust, out into the great open reach of the valley.

The driver, whose name I have forgotten, said nothing, nor did he slow the car until he brought it to an abrupt stop ten miles later at the gate of a rail fence that displayed signs of having once been whitewashed. Even then he did not speak. He only pointed to the door of a log and clapboard building.

He went ahead of us into the bunkhouse, and following him, I learned at last that he was capable of speech, for he spoke to the man in the washtub.

He said, "Hello, Mott. Got 'em bad again?"

The man in the washtub said: "Yep. Sore as a hoot owl's ass with a firecracker in it."

The driver waved a hand at several empty iron cots, a gesture apparently meant to convey instructions to us to make our own selections among them. Then he went out.

The man in the washtub, appearing to be quite oblivious to our presence or the activity of our getting settled, continued to splash the blue solution into his crotch.

39

It is quite possible, as any wanderer knows, to pass from one world into another only by stepping across a threshold. One does not easily forget such a transition. One long recalls the changes and the sensations and the thoughts which followed that single step.

With this insignificant occurrence I came for the first time to understand that there were two Wests.

There was the West of the mountains and the plains and the forests and the deserts. And there was the West of human life, of the people who lived and worked in these environments.

The curtain would open wider as time passed, and I would see portrayed the contrasts which gave spirit and function and color to the unfolding drama, the contrasts of history and legend, of fact and fiction, of romance and reality.

If there were nothing more than a threshold between these two Wests, passing across it was, nevertheless, comparable to leaving sunlight in which all the beauty of the earth was displayed, and entering shadows that fell from the ugliness of ignorance and obscenity and bigotry and hatred.

4

I T WAS THE OLD MEN I wanted to know, whom I wanted to hear talk, more than the others.

I did come to know a few well, and to gain the confidence of some of them, in Buffalo, Wyoming, in the Madison Valley, in Lodgegrass, and in the Crazy Woman Country, and the Big Horns, and out on the Beaverhead, and down in Santa Fe.

There were old men in those places . . . still working at something . . . who could talk about the fighting years, not only the fighting between the cattlemen and the sheepmen and the homesteaders, but the Indian wars. They had taken part in them.

I knew a good deal about these things, as I had an inherent love for western history. My father had nurtured it. Not only had he maintained a supply of books for me that would have benefited a public library, but always he had been available for a discussion, if not an argument, about western military campaigns and the conditions and forces which had brought the destruction of the Indian peoples. He liked especially to expound on the comparative qualifications and characters and abilities of the great chiefs and the generals who were their antagonists.

They were fine books he brought home . . . and there were portfolios of prints made from the drawings and paintings of Remington, and A.B. Frost, and Miller, and Catlin, and other noted western artists . . . books of history and memoirs and biographies, and the magnificent reports that came from such places as the American Museum of Natural History and the Bureau of American Ethnology of the Smithsonian Institution.

He had wanted me to take a suitcase of books with me when I first went west to work. He had suggested, among others, Chittenden's *History of the American Fur Trade,* and Parkman's *Oregon Trail,* and Bradbury's *Travels in the Interior of North America,* and Irving's *Astoria.* I had managed to veto the proposal. I took with me a volume he had only recently acquired and which I had only begun to read. It was Myers' *History of the Great American Fortunes.*

When I found out how indefinite would be my movements in the West, I was glad I had not taken them. A suitcase of books would not have been an easy burden for one engaged in extensive peripatetics. Moreover, I was sure that no one I met in the bunkhouses would have appreciated them.

The old men I was privileged to know were voices speaking from the past. They were, in the sense I considered them, living history.

So I was greatly pleased on a June morning when I was told to go with Brulé Kimball in the big wagon to the summer cow camp, which was in the mountains, west of the valley. I was pleased for two reasons. The trip would take me away for a few days from the hard monotonous work on the ranch, and it would make possible a close acquaintanceship with a

So I was greatly pleased on a June morning when I was told to go with Brulé Kimball in the big wagon to the summer cow camp . . .

man who had been a scout with the cavalry in the Powder River country six years before the arrogant, unconscionable Custer led his troops to disaster on the Little Big Horn.

It was my second summer in the Madison Valley. In that time I had come to understand something of what the war was doing to places like it, to all the western valleys in which water could be ditched from streams, and even in places where running water was not so easily obtainable and grain growers had to gamble that enough moisture would fall to make dry-farming operations successful.

The war was converting the West into a gigantic grain ranch. Every piece of ground in which it was believed a seed would sprout was being planted. The fields reached away in unbroken furrowed floors for miles.

Driving a service wagon, it might take me most of a morning to deliver a spare part to a disabled tractor. There were few roads, and an automobile could not travel over the rough range or the broken ground.

The tractors started each morning with the first light. In the middle of the day relief drivers would take them over. And they would roar on, the gang plows tearing up the grass that never before had been disturbed. They would roar on until darkness stopped them. Behind the tractors came the disks and the tooth harrows and the seeders, each contributing in its own way to the new West.

There were new dams and canals being constructed, and they would make it possible to get water on more ground, in higher places, on the great dry benches. Wheat and oats and rye and alfalfa would make a crazy quilt of the ranges. The grass that had supported the game herds upon which the Indians depended, and then the cattle and the sheep and the horses, would be forever gone.

This day I would deliver bags of seed to a designated place, a place lost in a sweep of newly turned earth that ran into the sky. The prairie chickens and the blue grouse had disappeared, frantic in their search for tall grass and brush, driven to higher ground and along the streams where thickets were still to be found. I would pile the sacks of seed and drive away. Although there was nothing to be seen but the raw exposed earth as far as my eyes could reach, I knew that sometime during the day, a planter would pass there and would refill his seeders.

This day I would deliver drums of tractor fuel.

This day I would be assigned to fill drinking water cans, and to take mail out to a specified drop for men I seldom saw.

A man named Rankin was the foreman. He asked me, "Did you ever drive a four-horse hitch?"

"Once."

He shook his head. "I can't spare no experienced man, God knows, but I can't let old Brulé go alone no more. Goddamn the old coot . . . " There was affection in his tone. ". . . he dozes off. That's a tough road up there. Ain't hardly more than two ruts in places, and it goes right through some spring bogs. You got to have four horses. I'd feel bad if old Brulé fell to sleep and drove right off a grade and got himself killed dead. Although his hide wouldn't be worth a nickel at an auction for sinners. You go with him. You'll have more than a ton on the wagon, an' that's too much for that road. But these supplies got to be took up there or them riders won't have nothin' to eat. Do like he says, an' keep him awake in the bad places. He'll take 'em through."

Brulé's eyes were bright blue stones in a mosaic of wrinkled tawny buckskin. He was small and thin . . . I thought I could have easily picked him up in my arms . . . seeming to be made of nothing more than skin and sinew stretched over a few bones. Yet he was lithe and there was a certain grace in his movements. I believed that he was as hard and as tough as a briar stem.

He was about seventy-five. When he first became a scout he was little more than twenty . . . old enough for the job. He had grown up in the Indian Country. His father had been a freighter, and the family had moved often when he was a boy. He came to know many parts of the country well . . . western Nebraska and western Kansas and what later became South Dakota, all of which he spoke of as being *way back east* . . . and many Indians. But his most vivid memories seemed to be of the Sioux in Dakota, where his father had a contract to deliver supplies to Army stations and reservations.

There had been a time when Brulé Kimball spoke the Hunkpapa and Oglalla dialects as well as he spoke English. He knew the Sioux. And they knew him. He knew Red Cloud and Gaul and Sitting Bull and several other Bulls and Low Dog and Crow King and Crazy Horse and several other Horses and some Wolves.

Brulé Kimball could read to some extent, but newspaper type was too small for his eyes to see with clarity, and he refused to wear glasses. Shortly before we left for the cow camp he had noticed the heading of a news story which said that Cable Winship had died in Cheyenne. It happened that I had read the dispatch, which appeared in a Bozeman paper, and although it was brief it contained the information that Cable Winship was a prominent cattleman, and that he had died as the result of a blow on the head delivered by an unidentified assailant on a Cheyenne street at night.

"Probably had it comin'," Brulé said. "I almost done it to him myself one time."

I had come to understand that casualness and patience were needed in talking with men like Brulé Kimball. They had a way of divulging things slowly, with pauses, as if they were considering their thoughts before revealing them. He had brought up the matter of Cable Winship, and I had the impression he had something to say about it, but I concealed my curiosity, and said only, "Did you work for him?"

"Hell, no," he said. "But I knew him, and too good to my likin'. He had a spread that reached from Cheyenne to Kingdom Come an' back. One o' the biggest anywheres. Knew his brother, too. Solon, his name was. He run evry gamblin' joint and whorehouse and saloon south o' Casper, I reckon. But I never did know him, Solon, too good. I never did gamble, an' never drunk much, and I never did take to whorehouses. Indin squaws suited me better. But Cable Winship I knowed when he was a captain." He mouthed his toothless gums. "That was a long time ago."

And there was that year . . . Brulé wasn't certain of the date, but is was "around 'seventy" . . . when spring had come early to the Powder River country. March had no more than gone before the ranges were like a tossing green sea breaking against the benchlands and the red buttes.

I would come to know that country. I would know the beauty of its spring. And it would still be cow country when I first saw it. There would still be roundup wagons running, operating in the old-time ways, and I would work for some big outfits. One of them would have a fenced area called the Horse Pasture which contained a hundred thousand acres between the Tongue and the Powder.

It was cow country still, but when Brulé was there in the seventies it was Indian country, and in the spring buffalo, not cows, were dropping calves that frisked on the warming slopes, and antelope streaked across the flatlands in ecstasy over new-found alarms, and elk and deer grazed on the foothills under the crystal and blue wall of the Big Horns that stood to the west.

When Brulé knew it, the wild contingents were there, the people who would not stay on reservations, the warriors who had sworn to fight to the death for justice and their last hunting grounds.

And that year of the early spring, with the Sioux's Moon of the Red Grass Appearing, they began to stir. Winter-bound muscles flexed with reviving strength. And a wild new spirit surged in blood, stirred by the promises of the awakening earth.

The red people danced, danced for the forays and the hunts to come, the young men burning with eagerness to be off on horse-stealing raids and dreaming of fresh scalps dripping over naked thighs, and the old men languishing in dreams of revenge they would never realize, and grieving in the mellowness and frailty of their fading days.

Fort Kearny stood in the afternoon shadows of the Big Horns. And scouts, couriers and supply trains coming into it from Fort Russell and the railroad, nearly three hundred miles south of the Crazy Woman country, brought intelligence that sobered faces. For as they pieced together the information they saw a disheartening picture. If there was a hope of peace in the summer ahead it existed only in the phlegmatic conceited minds of general-staff officers and bureaucrats safely ensconced behind desks in far-off Washington. The men at Fort Kearny would have wagered their last chance of eternal salvation that scalp-laden specters would ride beside them before the fall had come . . . if they lived that long. In 1868 they saw blood on the sun. And they heard war drums in their sleep.

That was the arena, the stage, which Brulé Kimball knew that year of the early spring.

A few May days had passed when Troops C and D, under the command of Captain Cable Winship, were en route back to the fort from a reconnaissance mission when they were attacked by a small band of renegade Sioux. The exchange of fire had lasted no more than five or six minutes. The attackers, obviously realizing the futility of a sustained assault, had done no more than strike and run.

But two troopers had been killed, and four had been wounded.

With the bodies of the dead men lashed over packsaddles, and two seriously wounded borne in litters suspended between horses, Captain Winship had moved on only far enough to reach a good defensive position beside a stream. There he made camp for the night, and waited impatiently for his two civilian scouts, Brulé Kimball and a half-breed named Gregg, to return from a reconnoiter in the surrounding country.

The scouts brought word that the raiders had fled and would not return. There had been only eight of them, and it was inconceivable that they would make a second attack against two troops of cavalry. Moreover, at least one of them had been wounded. Brulé had found bloodstains on a rock along the route over which they had fled.

Captain Winship did not agree with the deduction. He seemed unable to convince himself that his force was not in great danger, and he charged the scouts with being negligent in not discovering the Indians before the attack. He sneered at Brulé's defense that eight young bucks could scatter, and with the ground as damp as it was they would raise no dust, and could conceal themselves so cleverly that only an eagle could have spotted them.

Most of the night Captain Winship paced nervously, as if he expected at any moment a renewal of the assault. His voice was strained, and there was fury in it, and Brulé noticed that his hands trembled, and he appeared to be struggling to contain a tempest within himself.

"There was a reason for his frenzy," Brulé said to me. "It was his last duty. He was leaving the Army an' goin' to Cheyenne. I guess he was just plumb scared he wouldn't get there. He was afraid he would get a Sioux slug in his gut.

He had shit in his neck, was what it was. Hell, they was only a bunch of young red devils out for some fun. I never did think they had a mind to fight. Just rascallin' around, an' we happened to come along."

Shortly before dawn a soft brief rain fell. Captain Winship sent a sergeant to tell the scouts that the march would be resumed with the coming of the first light. Brulé got up and went to him and he suggested that under the conditions it would be better to wait until the sun had risen. But the captain rejected the advice with no more than a wave of his hand. He ordered Brulé and Gregg to precede the troops and scout the route. In a nasty tone he reminded Brulé that eyes and ears were useful things if properly used.

The day began with light gray mists obscuring the hills. In two files the troops moved slowly up the creek valley. They had gone no more than three miles when Brulé met them. He and Gregg had come upon a small Indian camp a short distance ahead. It contained no more than twenty tepees, and only a few, perhaps no more than a dozen, horses were grazing near it.

Captain Winship ordered preparations for an attack.

"Jumpin' Jesus," Brulé said to me, "I told him it was only a little village. We could just go around it without no trouble. Both me an' Gregg knowed it wasn't no war party. I told him it probly didn't have nobody in it but some women and children, an' maybe a few oldsters. We knowed it was just part of a meat camp, an' the men was off huntin'. But he wouldn't listen. He just says, 'Mr. Kimball, you and Mr. Gregg are relieved, if you don't wish to follow my orders.' He says he would file a report of our arguin' and disobeyin' him."

"And I says to myself, 'Don't take a crap, you dummy, 'cause you won't have no brains left if you do.' An' I just went off."

Brulé Kimball and Gregg watched the attack from an

53

adjacent rise. The troopers swept down on the village, firing as they went. It was obvious at once that the opinion of the scouts had been correct.

Dogs gave the alarm, but not before the troopers were close enough to shoot into the tepees. Only women, some of them carrying small children, ran out. The only return fire in the engagement came from two old men, and they were quickly cut down.

Some of the troopers were sickened by the sight, and vomited over themselves and their saddles. It was later told about the fort how a lieutenant had appealed to Captain Winship to halt the slaughter, and how Captain Winship, in reply, had spurred his horse toward a running woman who had an infant in her arms, and had shot her in the back, and then had shot the child as it fell from her grasp.

When there was no more life in sight, Captain Winship had the tepees burned. With the smoke rising he appeared to be satisfied, and he gave orders to continue to the fort.

Brulé and Gregg reckoned that no less than fifteen women and five elderly men had been slain. A dozen youngsters, ranging from infants to ten or twelve years in age, had been senselessly butchered. They knew that some of the villagers had escaped into the thickets that bordered the creek, but they could not be certain how many had been spared.

Brulé and Gregg rode hard for the fort. Their only thought was to put the scene behind them as quickly as possible. They needed no seer or medicine man to predict the events of the immediate future.

Two days later Captain Winship's Army career ended.

He might have waited to travel to Fort Russell with a strong supply train. But the commanding officer, sickened by the insane attack on the village and fully aware of the reprisals he must face, knew that reinforcements must be sent to him as swiftly as possible. He wanted dispatches to go out at once.

Brulé agreed to take them, if he were given eight experienced troopers who were ordered to abide by his decisions. The colonel assigned a sergeant and seven men to the mission.

Captain Winship asked to go with them. Brulé didn't want him . . . he would have liked it if he had never seen him again . . . but he complied with the C.O.'s request to take him. The colonel made no secret of his desire to see Captain Winship depart.

It was almost midnight when the ten men rode quietly out of Fort Kearny. There was no moon but the brilliant stars provided light enough to outline dimly the big shoulders of the surrounding hills.

Three troopers led lightly loaded packhorses. Captain Winship remained near the center of the file. Directly behind Brulé, who led the way, was the sergeant, a Texan named Ways.

They rode steadily at a brisk walk. Brulé was a small hunched figure with a greasy knot of long black hair, tied in the manner of a Sioux. He moved ahead unhesitantly, for he knew well the trail he had chosen. Occasionally he would come to an abrupt stop, and without command the men behind him would stop. And he would sit motionless until he chose to go on. No one spoke, for Brulé had warned them he would tolerate no unnecessary conversation. If anything needed to be said, he would say it. He understood very well the chance he was taking, and under the strain of the realization he was tense and irascible.

When they stopped at a small stream for a brief rest and to let the horses drink, he said with obvious concern, "It's so still tonight you could hear a piss ant cough."

The east was tinted with the rising sun when Captain Winship disclosed his supposition that they would conceal themselves through the day.

"You ain't givin' orders no more," Brulé said, "but if

55

you want to conceal yourself, it's all right with me."

They rode on in silence, and Brulé said nothing of his wish to reach a resting place he knew would be advantageous in the event they were discovered.

The morning was immaculate in its clearness. The sun was an hour high when one of the horses fell into a series of stumbles.

The trooper riding it quickly dismounted. And he said, "Brulé, this horse can't go no further without rest."

"I knew that an hour ago," Brulé said.

"Do we have to kill a good animal?"

"Yes," Brulé said, and stared into distance, as if he were ascertaining their exact location.

Captain Winship said, "Do you see something?"

Brulé ignored him and spoke quietly to the trooper standing beside the crippled horse. "Put your saddle on that bay, and spread the pack among us."

The men stood wearily beside their mounts while the transfer was made.

Then Brulé said, "Go ahead."

"Go ahead, what?" the trooper said.

"We can't have no cripple trailin' us, or tryin' to," Brulé said.

The trooper said with anger, "Shoot it yourself. That's a good . . ."

"Christ!" Brulé said. "Who said shoot? There will be no gunfire." Quickly he stepped to a packhorse and drew an axe from its sheath.

The horse collapsed under the first blow. He struck again and split its skull. Blood gushed from its nostrils and mouth.

As he replaced the bloody axe, he motioned to the men to move on, and he said, "Nothin' but bones soon."

The magpies would get the eyes before they were cold. And the buzzards would soon pick up the scent or sight the carcass. But the wolves would fight them off until they had had their fill.

An hour later they forded a stream, and after passing through a narrow defile came out on the brink of a benchland. There they had a long view of the country.

In time I would go there, and I would know its magnificence, the immense wall of the Big Horns, and along the South Fork of Crazy Woman Creek the cottonwoods would drop white tufts that make the ground appear to be covered with forgotten patches of snow, and the stirring air would carry the spice of blooming sage and the fragrance of blossoming cedars, and myriads of little flowers would brighten the hill slopes. And the larks would sing, and the cranes and sandpipers and blackbirds and curlews would populate the little meadows and marshes, and the killdeers would cry their shrill alarms. And I would remember an eagle homing into the falling sun and the shadows of the angular walls and buttes lying on the rolling earth like enormous jagged pieces of great blue pillars and temples that had toppled and broken.

But then, when Brulé was there, the beauty of the country was overshadowed by lurking death.

"No fire," he said. "Break out some biscuits and grease, or whatever it is we got to eat."

The horses cropped the fine grass at the mouth of the defile and rested in the shade. From the brink of the bench the men watched for a sign that would warn them of danger. This was the vantage place Brulé had wanted to reach.

The sergeant said, "How do we go now?"

Brulé had respect for the sergeant . . . a fine able trooper. He said, "Along the mountains as straight as we can. If we have good luck, in two more nights we should reach a village of Moon Dog's people. He's a kind of bastard. Mostly Cheyenne, but he's always run with the Shoshone. That's what his mother was, at least part. Big man, Moon Dog. Ain't nobody disputes him much. He's my friend, too. I done him a good turn. They sent a troop out to guard the track workers on the new railroad. If they had treated Moon Dog right and decent he wouldn't a bothered them none. He knew he couldn't stop the railroad. Hellfire, he ain't no fool, and he would just as leave try to stop the sun from comin' up. I told 'em what to do to stop the stealin' but they wouldn't heed me. They just kept reportin' that Moon Dog was on the warpath, and I knowed he weren't. Such crap. They shoulda seen a warpath. So they kept shootin' if they saw a shadow they thought was a buck, and the result was that they didn't kill no Indians, but they got seven troopers killed during that summer, an' one whore shot in the butt.

"At that, they was lucky. It would have been worse if I hadn't a gone out by myself and seen Moon Dog. There was a lot o' wagons had come in, people followin' the railroad builders. So I made arrangements with Moon Dog to let some o' his bucks steal a wagon load o' supplies. For that he agreed to keep 'em away from us till spring.

"But they took the wrong wagon. It weren't food they wanted, anyway. Only the wagon they took by mistake belonged to a madam and her outfit. Called the Paris Boudoir. And that was when she got creased right across her fat ass, when they was makin' off with her wagon. Because she tried to stop 'em, the silly bitch.

"The wagon was big, an' it was loaded with all sorts o' things, a tent or two and trunks and doodads an' such for her girls. But there was an old brass bed in it which she had brought all the way from Omaha. She could get fifty cents extra if a man wanted to use one o' her strumps on it, because that was real class.

"By God, you never seen nobody as mad as that old chippy when she lost that brass bed. She threatened to cut off my balls if she ever got me in her place.

"Anyway, she never did, an' the stealin' stopped, an' there weren't no more shootin' that summer. It was the brass bed that done it.

"Ol' Moon Dog was as happy with it as a dog with two tails. I reckon him and his squaw slept a long time in it."

And in the afternoon, from the brink of the bench, they saw the moving dust. Lying down they watched intently as it came nearer. It came within two miles of them, to the east, and they could see horses and riders bunched closely together.

And then it vanished toward the south.

Captain Winship knelt beside Brulé. Once more his hands were trembling, and there was terror in his eyes. "Who are they?" he said.

"How the hell would I know who they are?" Brulé said.

"They're looking for us," the captain said.

"Maybe," Brulé said. "Maybe not. One thing: they ain't found our trail or they wouldn't be showin' themselves that way and movin' that fast. Another thing: they ain't no village travelin', because they ain't got no travois. You don't go that fast with travois and a lot o' squaws and kids and things. An' that might not be so good for us."

"They'll be ahead of us," the captain said. "I think we should go back to the fort as fast as we can. There must have been fifty of them."

"You do?" Brulé said. "What you think don't matter none to me no more."

"But it's sensible," the captain said. "I must insist . . ."

"You must what?" Brulé said.

The captain appeared desperate as he said, "I'm sure the sergeant will agree with me. We'd be riding into a trap, if we went on south. We'd be cut off."

The sergeant said slowly, "I reckon I'll do whatever Brulé says."

"But we're riding right into a trap!" the captain said, and he looked wildly from one to the other. "We can't do it!"

Brulé got up and stepped to a pack. Blood was dried on the blade of the axe he took up.

He stood before Captain Winship as he said, "See this? You know what I did to that horse? I'd just as soon do the same thing to a man with piss for blood."

The captain did not reply. He only stared at Brulé.

In the early dusk they rode on.

Brulé and I were having our lunch in the shadow of the wagon, on the way to the cow camp, and the four horses were munching placidly in their nose bags, when he said, "I knowed Cable Winship, all right. We got down to Moon Dog's, an' then we was safe enough. Cabe Winship never even said good-by when he left us.

"He built up this big cow outfit with his brother's whorehouse an' gamblin' and saloon money. I think I did hear that he went to Congress for a term or two. He had enough to buy him a seat from the governor.

"I just hope it was some Indin who hit him on the head."

5

THERE WAS THAT EARLY SUMMER when I went to work on the ranch on Shields River, above Willsal. It was a beautiful country with the Crazy Mountains standing up against the east, their feet wrapped in the folds of dark green forests.

The bunkhouse was worse than some in which I had lived. The foreman didn't like anybody who was born east of the Mississippi River, and he let me know it. But the food was good, and I decided to stay long enough to get a little money in my pocket.

He drove me out in a truck that morning, and he told me to patrol an irrigation ditch, to remove rocks and weeds and dirt that might have fallen into it.

He handed me a twenty-two rifle and a box of cartridges, and he said, "Shoot any jacks or prairie dogs or badgers, anything like that you see. There's gettin' to be too many pests up here, an' they dig burrows, an' then the water breaks into them, an' wastes. I'm bringin' out some poison grain soon, but we'll have to shoot 'em until it gets here."

He drove away. I felt the heaviness of the silence. It was as if the big mountains were pressing down on the country, crushing all sounds. But some sounds survived, little sounds and beautiful sounds, like a lark's song and the rustling of the tall grass and the whir of a blue grouse's wings.

I walked slowly along the ditch with my shovel and my pitchfork and the gun. The water was seldom interrupted. It ran smoothly and steadily toward its appointed destination . . . wherever that was.

Great white thunderheads gathered over the peaks. To the west a storm mounted in blue-black clouds. I heard the hail long before it reached me. I heard it first as a low ominous rumbling. Then I saw it coming up the valley, an immense dark blue broom swung from the sky and sweeping the earth. The rumble became a roar. I ran toward a headgate which stood at the end of a branch ditch, and crawled under it on the dry side.

The hail had almost reached me when I saw suddenly that I had company. An immense jack rabbit scurried into the headgate and sat beside me. His bloodshot eyes fastened on my face. But it was not an unfriendly look. One of his ears had been torn, and there were scars on his head and his haunches. I thought he must have been in a lot of battles.

We sat there together while the hail roared over us. It made the earth tremble, and it sounded like bullets striking the planks of the headgate. Some of the hailstones were as large as eggs. Both of us might have been killed had it not been for that shelter.

It ended as abruptly as it had come, sweeping on to destroy itself against the walls of the benchlands and the mountains.

Just before he leaped away the big rabbit glanced at me. There could be no mistaking the gratefulness in his eyes.

And I was just as grateful to him . . . for the trust he had placed in me.

*I walked slowly along the ditch with my
shovel and my pitchfork and the gun.*

6

THE HOME RANCH was near Sheridan, in Wyoming.
It was a big outfit. Some of the cattle ranged north
into the Crow Reservation, and that was in Montana. More
than two hundred thousand acres were leased from the Crows,
and they were fine grasslands.

The auto stage dropped me off at the gate to a big yard
through which a gravel walk ran between reaches of lawn
and flower beds to a large white house with two wings extending from it. I stood there several minutes before a man emerged
from the side door of a small building. He took a few steps
toward me, and he was somewhat stooped and he wore highly
polished boots and tan gabardine pants with a sharp crease
in them and a clean white shirt.

"Come in here, please," he said.

I left my bedroll and suitcase and followed him into an
office.

"There doesn't seem to be anybody else around just now,"

he said as he went through a small gate in a partition and stood behind a counter. "Anyway, I want to get your name and so on." He smiled. "I suppose you were sent out here to work."

"Yes," I said. "Quite a nice place . . ."

"Oh, yes." He asked my name and wrote it on a page of a ledger. "You're on the payroll. It's . . ." He glanced at a clock. "About eleven. No use trying to start you this morning. Come along."

As we walked across a wide stretch of bare earth that ran to some corrals and stables, he said, "I'll show you the bunkhouse. The foreman will be here for dinner, I expect." Then he added, as if he thought the explanation necessary, "I'm just the bookkeeper."

The bunkhouse was a white stucco, ell-shaped building with a red tile roof, and there were geraniums blooming in boxes beneath its windows, and it had a screen door. These embellishments were unusual, but the interior was nothing less than amazing.

Along two walls of a large room stood rows of white iron beds, each with a table and a chair beside it. And there were other chairs, large and comfortable, upholstered in a heavy brown corded fabric, standing about a wide table which was littered with magazines and books and newspapers. In a corner was an octagonal poker table covered with a green cloth on which were strewn several decks of cards and a number of chips.

He pointed to two beds. There were mattresses on them. "I'm sure neither of these is in use," he said. "Take whichever . . ." He stopped speaking and hurried through a doorway. I heard the swishing of water. "Some of the men simply cannot remember to flush the toilet," he said, and gave a short laugh, as if he were both provoked and amused. "I guess some of them can't get used to having it . . . inside, I mean."

Then he added quickly, "But they're all good men, very good men. Well, make yourself at home. There will be someone here before dinner to tell you what to do."

My astonishment prevailed. And it was increased when I looked into a smaller room and found there two shower baths and a tub. The tub looked as if it needed cleansing. And the towels that draped several racks appeared to have escaped laundering for some time.

When I heard a footfall, I turned quickly, and I saw a rather heavy man in wrinkled blue overalls. He nodded, threw a battered hat on a bed, and in a pleasant voice said, "I run the sheep here. Name's Frank Gower. Got forty thousand head up on the hills this year."

We shook hands, and my dominant thought emerged in words, "I never saw anything like this on a ranch," I said.

He smiled and dropped into a chair and he said, "No, an' I guess you wouldn't, even if you went all over the whole dang country. But it ain't what it was once. She kind o' gave up on some things."

"Who?" I said.

"The woman the old man married when he went back east that time. About four year ago. Somewheres in Virginia or New York or one o' them places." He got up. "Well, I guess I'll wash for dinner. You can get a towel from the chicken wrangler." And then he added, as if he felt he might be intruding, "If you want one. But you can use one o' them in there this time . . . if you need it. He ain't around, nohow."

The information came to me in dibs and dabs from several men, and over a period of weeks.

The old man had gone east one fall to visit some friends. When he returned to the ranch in the spring he had a new wife. And then things began to happen. Painters and carpenters and stonemasons and plumbers arrived from Sheridan and even from as far away as Billings. The wings were built on the house, and it was painted. And the gravel walk was constructed, and the flowers were planted. And a new orchard was set out, back of the big corrals. And the old bunkhouse was torn down, and the men were obliged to sleep in the barn or outdoors while the new building was constructed.

"Hell, they was embarrassed when they saw where they had to live," a rider said. "Ain't none of them never lived in such a place, I reckon. It was the sheets which caused the first real trouble."

She had insisted that sheets not only be provided, but that they be changed twice a week.

"But they couldn't get nobody to change them," the stable boss said. "Couldn't get no woman to go in the bunkhouse to do it, and sweep out, and put clean towels, like she wanted done. Shit, they wasn't used to sheets, includin' me, too. Most o' them never slept on a sheet in their life. Some o' them just threw the sheets in a corner. Like one o' them said, you slipped around too much on them. Blankets was good enough. First thing you know, like old Charlie would say, she'll want us to wear nightshirts and take a bath every day."

The old man persuaded her to discontinue the sheets. But she refused to permit the bright flowered curtains to be taken down from the windows. And she insisted on installing rust-colored rugs . . . one beside each bed . . . which she said could be washed in the laundry house she had built.

Someone overheard her and the old man talking.

"How can they have any privacy without curtains at the windows?" she asked.

"I don't think that worries them," he said.

"Well, it should," she said.

"Yes, ma'am," he said.

Whenever he said that she seemed to be deeply irritated. "I do wish you'd stop saying 'Yes, ma'am,'" she said.

"All right," he said. "There's somethin' we forgot."

72

*"I run the sheep here. Name's Frank Gower.
Got forty thousand head up on the hills this
year."*

"What?" she said.

"Sandboxes," he said. "I told Ed to make them a couple."

"What in the world for?" she said. "They're not cats, are they? I put in two of the largest wastebaskets I could find."

"Well, they need some place to spit," he said. "It's inconvenient to have to get up an' spit out the door, specially if it's cold an' it's closed. They wouldn't want to spit in a wastebasket. Got too much manners."

"I think it's simply disgusting," she said.

"Yes, ma'am," he said.

"Oh, for goodness sakes!" she said.

The sheets disappeared. The sandboxes were installed. But not all men had good aims. The rugs remained. But no one washed them, and when they got caked with mud they were kicked under beds. The curtains hung until they were limp and dirty. And then they, too, vanished.

The chicken wrangler was told to clean the tub and the showers and the flush toilet. But he refused, and quit.

A new chicken wrangler came, but he was only instructed to sweep out the bunkhouse once a week, and to keep a supply of towels available. The cleaning of the bathtub was left up to anyone who wished to do it. And it became stained with the minerals in the water and rings of soapy dirt. But most men used the showers for baths, when they took them, and no one seemed to think that cleaning a shower was necessary.

No one would clean the toilet, either, until its odor became unbearable. Then the chicken wrangler would pour some kind of dark liquid generously into the bowl and over the seat and the surrounding floor. After that drastic measure was completed, the entire bunkhouse smelled like a freshly disinfected jail.

"I reckon she kind o' give up," a man said. "Kind o' give up on the mess house, too. Time was that she insisted that we have a lot o' salad on little plates, and de-sert served in

75

side dishes, an' clean tablecloths and napkins evry meal. Hell-to-breakfast, these fellows didn't want no more than one plate and one cup for everything. Now we just eat sensible, like any outfit."

The stable boss threw a saddle on a horse. And he said, "I don't reckon he ever says 'Yes, ma'am' to her no more. At least, I ain't heard him say it for a long while."

7

E WERE GOING TO RIDE that day along some ridges of the Bridger Mountains. Our assignment was to see if some cattle which had been turned into the area a fortnight before had strayed beyond the summer grazing grounds that the ranch leased from the Forest Service.

Going with Abe Bowman was a duty I welcomed. He was one of the best cowboys in Montana, and I hoped that I would not only get to know him better but that I would learn something from him about line riding. It was a type of work in which I had little experience.

As we left the corral at the cow camp the sun had not yet reached into the valleys, and their lush green was shrouded in mists. Suddenly the big black Abe Bowman rode dropped its head and bucked several times. He laughed boyishly, and said, "He just likes to do that, but he don't mean nothin' by it. These chilly mornings his back itches, an' he just feels good." He patted the horse's neck. "You can't throw me, you cantankerous son-of-a-bitch, an' you know it."

We got to talking about the war as we rode along, and I mentioned receiving a letter from my mother in which she had written about the terrible atrocities in Belgium.

"It makes me wish I could go and fight," I said.

Abe said, "I heard tell they don't use much cavalry in this war."

"I guess not," I said. "The fighting is on the sea and in trenches."

"I wouldn't be no good at either," he said. "Boats make me sick to look at, and I'd be a mighty poor soldier on foot. Believe I'd just set down, come Germans or Chinamen. I only had one pair o' shoes I can remember in my life, when I was a little kid in school. Mamma tried to make me wear 'em, but I'd take 'em off an' go barefoot, if I couldn't wear my boots, like my papa done."

Abe Bowman was twenty-three, but he was a man with exceptionally powerful arms and shoulders. He had a broad brown face that easily broke into a smile. His voice was soft. He rode as if he were sitting in a rocking chair. I marveled at his ability to pick out cattle which I had not noticed on distant ridges and mountain meadows.

My mother also had written about the flu deaths at Great Lakes, and while we were eating our cold lunch I read excerpts from that part of her letter:

"Father has just told me of his awful experience at Great Lakes. He was there today about some contractor's payroll insurance. He had to wear a mask. The coffins were stacked high. There were hundreds of people about the main gate, friends and relatives of the sailors. Women stood all along the high fence screaming and crying to get in to their sons. Some of the women collapsed. He is terribly depressed tonight, and he said he would never forget the sobbing and the pleading of the women to be let in. As I write this, I feel like crying, crying out to God to tell us why such things must be . . ."

*Going with Abe Bowman was a duty I wel-
comed. He was one of the best cowboys in
Montana...*

Abe shook his head. And he said, "Hell of a mess, ain't it?" Then he got up. "Well, let's go. It'll be dusk when we get back."

It was the evening of the next day when Abe dropped down beside me as I was sitting in front of the bunkhouse. And he said in his quiet way, "You got more education than me. I get sort o' confused about the country. Down below the Beaverhead you go into Idaho. I know that. What's next?"

"Utah."

"Then what?"

"Arizona."

"That's by Mexico, ain't it?"

"Yes."

And then he said, "I been thinkin' about goin' down there, an' maybe stay all next winter. They tell me it's warm in the winter, an' a lot o' nice friendly girls."

"I've never been to Mexico."

We sat in silence for a few moments. And then he said, "Would you want to go?"

"To Mexico?"

"That's right."

"You're not thinking of riding all the way!"

"I ain't thinkin' o' walkin'. I got six good horses of my own out here in the meadow."

"It would take months."

He only nodded.

"I'll have to give it a little thought," I said.

"Okeh. Tell me in the mornin'," he said. And he walked away.

I lay awake for some time that night. My body ached with weariness, but sleep was prevented by thoughts of riding to Mexico from Montana. What a great adventure! And even when sleep came, I did not rest well.

The next morning he was sitting alone on a log near the

cook wagon drinking a cup of coffee when I told him that I had decided not to go with him. My excuse was that I wanted to go home in the fall, and I needed to earn the money to pay my fare.

All he said in reply was, "Okeh." And he smiled and blew on his coffee to cool it.

I cut firewood for the cook that morning. And when I came back to the camp at noon all the riders were out, and only the foreman and the cook were there. We were eating when two men rode in. They were forest rangers. The cook told them to take plates and help themselves to food.

"Potatoes and meat in that big pot," the cook said. "Good side beef."

"That's what he calls it," the foreman said, "but I seen him out huntin' ground squirrels last night."

The forest rangers laughed. And while we ate they talked about the grass and the condition of the cattle and the dryness which posed a serious fire threat.

When one of them had finished his lunch he dropped his utensils into a tub of water, provided for that purpose, and he said in a casual way, "Do you have a man named Abe Bowman workin' here?"

"Did have," the foreman said. "He quit this mornin'. Took his things an' rode off."

"Don't know where he went, do you?"

"He didn't say."

The ranger lighted a stubby pipe, and seemed to be considering his thoughts.

"Did you want to see him?" the foreman said.

"Not specially," the ranger said. "It's really none of our business, I guess. But the federal marshal called up yesterday, and asked us to see if he was up here some place. The marshal wanted us to ask him to come in, if we ran onto him."

"What's he done?" the foreman said.

"Draft," the marshal said. "I guess he's been keepin' out o' the way some time. There's a warrant for him."

I knew then that Abe Bowman had left on his long ride to Mexico.

But I never did know why I had decided not to go with him.

8

THE BIG HORN COUNTRY had a hold on me. I would quit good jobs in other places to go back, although I couldn't have told anyone why I did it . . . I just wanted to. The same thing would happen in later years in New Mexico and Arizona. Suddenly I would want to be back there, especially in or close to the Navajo Country, and I would leave wherever I was and head for Santa Fe or Flagstaff, without excuse or plan.

That summer I went back to Buffalo from Idaho, and I went to work riding for the 76, one of the oldest outfits in Wyoming. Three weeks later a mean jugheaded little sorrel tried to throw me on some rocks and fell down. I got out of the saddle all right, but my left arm was fractured just above the wrist. They took me to a doctor in Buffalo, and when I returned, wearing a cast and sling, the foreman told me I could work around the ranch on foot, doing whatever I could with my good arm.

Although I shouldn't want to say it was a lucky break, under any other circumstances I most probably would never have got to know Fred Garvey as well as I did. They didn't call Fred a chicken wrangler or a handyman . . . not to his face, anyway. He had the high title of *corral boss*. That meant he had charge of the stables and the corrals and the horses and the supplies and the hay and the harness . . . and the chickens. But the boss's wife gathered the eggs, except when there were some in the mangers. Then Fred would go in and get them, for the horses in there weren't used to the smell of a woman or the rustle of skirts.

Fred Garvey wasn't old, perhaps fifty, but he looked a lot older, and that was because he had suffered a great deal. About six or seven years before I met him, his horse had been dragged down when he was roping during branding. He got caught in the rope. His pelvis and some other bones were broken. He would never be able to ride again, the doctors told him, but they fixed him up so he could get around. He was strong as a mule, but he walked bent over, and I think he was often in pain, although I never heard him complain.

"You just kind of hep him until you get well," the foreman said. "But don't try to do too much of his work. He kind of likes to do things by himself, in his own way. Don't interfere, because he's got a temper like a whirlwind."

Fred Garvey didn't have a temper. He had a mind that they didn't understand. He was insatiably curious. They thought he was angry when he questioned things, but that was not true. He simply had no patience with inefficiency or stupidity. He didn't like me at first, and he acted as if he didn't like the idea of me hanging around.

"What can I do?" I said.

"What I tell you," he said.

"Okeh," I said. "I'll wait in the bunkhouse until you tell

88

*Three weeks later a mean jugheaded little
sorrel tried to throw me on some rocks and
fell down.*

me." I was lying down, and everyone else was gone, when he came in and sat down.

"You read a lot," he said.

"I don't have much to read here."

He went over to his bunk, pulled out a book, and handed it to me. Its title was *The Beef Bonanza: How To Get Rich on the Plains.*

"Ever read that?" he said.

"Yes," I said. "That's an old book. I don't think it would be useful now."

He almost jerked it out of my hand, turned away, and threw it back in his bunk. "It's a lot of crap," he said. "I borrowed it from a friend of mine down in Cheyenne."

"You're right," I said.

"About what?" he said.

"It's a lot of crap. It came out sometime in the eighties. That was the time of the big storm," I said.

He gave a start and stared at me with a penetrating gaze. "It don't tell nothin' about it," he said. "What do you know about that?"

"Only what I've read," I said.

"I can tell you something about that," he said, and went out.

During the days my fracture was healing, and itching like hell under the plaster where I couldn't scratch it, we talked about the time of the beef bonanza. I knew he wanted to talk about the big storm before he did, but I didn't press him. I think he was feeling me out . . . a young punk who might have a mouth bigger than his brain. Sometimes we talked out in the corral, and sometimes, if it was raining, we talked in the saddle room, and sometimes we sat in front of the old log bunkhouse that had been there long before the beef bonanza had been written. There usually wasn't anyone around during most of the day, for the riders were out, and we had the place pretty much to ourselves.

He said one afternoon when we were putting hay in the mangers, "You hear these old cowmen say that the homesteaders ruined the country. Well, that's only part true. The storm had a lot to do with changin' things, and twernt nothin' changed in favor of the homesteaders, nor nobody else, for that matter. The storm brought the biggest change in this country, and nobody who lived through it can say it didn't."

"You did?" I said.

He nodded, and sat silent. I thought: The big storm occurred only about thirty-five or thirty-six years ago. It was possible that he could remember it well, and I said, "Where did you live then?"

He didn't answer my question directly. He said, "The history of this country wouldn't have been the same if it hadn't happened, I'll tell you that. The govermint might have had to put down a real fight. What do you call it? A civil war. There was real trouble shapin' up between the homesteaders and the big outfits. O' course, in most places the cowmen had the state legislators and the law officers on their side. They was murderin' and hangin' settlers, and burnin' their homes and destroyin' their property. It become so bad in some places that they had to send federal marshals in to keep order, but some of them was crooked and took bribes. Then . . . it was the summer of eighty-five . . . the storm come, and before it was over two years later both the cowmen and the homesteaders was thinkin' a lot less about fightin' each other than they was of findin' ways to stay alive. I know . . ."

Only a few widely separated parts of the West in that summer of 1885 suffered from abnormal dryness. The autumn, from northern Texas to Montana, was pleasant. Cowboys rode on the fall roundups through clear brisk days and through mild starry nights. And even though market prices were weak, cattlemen were optimistic. Always before that the market had recovered from slumps.

The fine weather continued until late fall. Not a few cattlemen held back shipments, anticipating an increase in prices. December had come before any appreciable amount of snow fell. Even then storms were short, and bright sun and strong winds kept the grass open. In general, stock were holding both strength and beef.

As the new year began, light rains fell throughout most of the high plains . . . precipitation in an unusual warmth. But gradually the downfalls turned to sleet. The Rocky Mountains became enveloped in an ominous dark curtain. And as the thermometer continued to drop, the ground froze.

Then down from Canada came howling gales. And on them rode one of the worst blizzards ever known in the Cow Country.

For days at a time the gale-driven blizzards raged. And the white hands of death reached far down into Texas.

For the first time in the memory of the oldest cowboys, range cattle, searching desperately for shelter and grass, invaded towns. The streets of such Cow Country centers as Miles City and Cheyenne and Great Falls and Dodge City were filled with freezing starving animals. They dropped dead at the doors of stores and homes and saloons.

The range cattle, not without instincts which had guided their wild predecessors, the buffalo, drifted southward, their rumps to the storm. Some of them traveled hundreds of miles, only to die in arroyos and canyons and in the ice of rivers. Some streams were bridged with carcasses. And the drift fences took the lives of thousands. For cattle piled up against them and froze to death. There were places where the crush had become so great that fences were torn down for miles. And still the cattle came, stumbling on over ice-hardened bodies.

"I recollect," Fred Garvey said, "that the paper told how more than ten thousand head had died along one drift fence in southern Kansas and the Oklahoma Panhandle. A Nebraska company lost a hundred thousand head. Hellfire, a loss o' fifty per cent wasn't nothin'."

In every state of the Cow Country the human toll was also heavy. Families of settlers were found frozen to death in cabins. Freighters died beside their teams. Various reports estimated the loss of life between three and four hundred men, women and children.

Fred Garvey said, "All the time you was hearin' about people who had disappeared, and you didn't need to be told what happened to them. For Christ's sake, we was findin' skeletons for years."

Before the great blizzard subsided in February, 1886, thermometer readings of fifty degrees below zero were commonplace. And there were several towns where the mercury had fallen to sixty below.

Some cattlemen, especially those who had borrowed heavily to expand, lost their holdings and went out of business.

"Everybody was bad hurt," Fred Garvey said, "but you can't kill hope in a good cowman. The grass was still there, weren't it? It would come back. It always had. Nothin' could kill off good bunch grass."

And there was money to be had for rebuilding. But, of course, bankers took advantage of the situation and raised interest rates to exorbitant levels.

"A lot o' ranchers got hurt by that, too," he said, "because, even though the storm was the worst ever known, they thought it might be a good sign in itself. It drove out an' killed a lot o' homesteaders. And they reckoned that it was unlikely another anywheres near as bad would come again for years, if ever."

The snow was gone in March. And the days grew warm and balmy. And the spring wind had the feel of early summer. The new grass started under favorable conditions. But the needed rains failed to come. And drying prematurely, the grass remained short. An unusual number of prairie fires filled the days with smoke haze and lighted the nights with eerie red glares.

By midsummer the skies were like hot metal. And the cottonwood leaves hung in yellow dryness, rustling in the scorching airs. When a strong wind blew, it was like a burning dehydrated blast that baked a man's throat and made him fear suffocation.

"Course the calf crop had been little, because of what happened the winter before," Fred said. "Now the ones that was born just fell and died right under the cows."

A vast land which in most summers brought an endless sea of rich amber grass was becoming an uninhabitable desert. The little streams were vanishing, leaving in their places ugly scars, cracked and white where alkali remained after the last drop of water had vanished. Most of the large streams were hardly more than trickles.

By early autumn the last of the tree leaves had curled and fallen, and bare limbs were raised to a hot azure sky. In the high countries the pine needles had turned red, and the chinky pins were wizened and impotent, and the cedars were dying like bent wrinkled old women.

The wild game was gone. There were no birds, except vultures and buzzards, for the waterholes were seared depressions, and the seeds and the insects had been destroyed.

Fred Garvey said, "I ain't never forgot the old Indin that come along by our place, an' he had his squaw and a bunch o' papooses in a old wagon with a bony team. He was gettin' out, 'cause if a man is goin' to live in a desert, he might as well live in a good one, an' he was goin' clear to New Mexico or somewheres down there where his squaw had some relations. 'No good,' he says. 'No good this country no more.' He says,

'Animals and birds go. Bad time come.' And he weren't wrong, by God."

First in the south, where the drought was the worst, and then in the north, the cattlemen tried to get the remainder of their herds to the railroads. Some drove north to Canada, where the ranges had suffered less damage. But most of them shipped the animals they were able to save to Omaha and Kansas City and Chicago.

The bottom fell out of the market, which was glutted with poor stock.

The fall was a procession of clear burning days. Orange heat waves rolled over the ranges. And like an immense ball of fire the sun rose, moved in a flaming path over the stricken earth, and dropped in a copper conflagration behind purple mountains. The stars welled up in a dense brilliant fog.

And there was no relief from the punishment, no change in the disastrous scheme of things.

It was a phenomenon born of a conspiracy of the elements.

October came with the heat of midsummer, as if the cycle of the seasons had been disrupted by some supernatural force.

In this way the second act of the great western tragedy closed.

When the curtain rose again, completely different scenery was revealed.

Seldom did deep snow come to the Cow Country before December. But now heavy snows fell in some sections in October. And throughout the West storms and gales raged in November.

The storms continued, following quickly one upon another. If none of them equaled the great blizzard of the previous year, their constancy had the same devastating effect.

Now, for the first time, the Cow Country knew birds whose natural habitat was the Arctic.

The fall was a procession of clear burning days.

The toll of human lives surpassed that of the year before. Wolves tore at the bodies.

Where the cattle still living staggered through the snow it was red with their blood. And their hides were covered with frozen blood, their legs raw from ice cuts and their hooves torn off in mad attempts to paw through the solid sheath to grass. Some of the animals which miraculously survived had ragged patches of hide hanging where wolves had eaten at them. But with so much meat available the wolves had not bothered to kill them.

On January 9, snow fell in Montana an inch an hour for sixteen hours. And the mercury hovered at twenty below zero. But there were places in the West where the temperature did not rise above forty below for periods of two weeks.

Suddenly, late in January, a chinook struck. Within a few hours the ranges were seas of slush, the streams roaring muddy torrents. It was a respite that saved thousands of cattle . . . but not for long.

As suddenly . . . as if they had been merely resting to gain their second wind . . . the elements resumed their assault. The worst storm of the winter swept in from the northwest. And it was late in March before the flinty ice had begun to melt in a spring thaw.

"I swear, a man could walk from the Black Hills clear across the Powder River country and on to the Big Horns without ever steppin' offa dead critters," Fred said.

If this was an exaggeration, the average of ninety per cent losses for the cattle companies was not.

Blizzard, drought, blizzard, and then, as if the disaster had never occurred, normal weather, strong green grass, balmy days, bright new leaves . . . normal, except for the smell of rotting carcasses and the human skeletons.

From coast to coast, newspapers and agricultural journals

cried that the range cattle business was forever dead. But they were wrong.

There was still lots of money in the nation's banks. And there were still cattle in south Texas, in every eastern and southern state, in California and Oregon and Washington. They could be bought for restocking the high plains. And they would be brought into the Cow Country by the train load. And there would be trail herds moving northward along the foothills of the mountains. And there would be hay for winter feeding, alfalfa and timothy shipped from the Middle West and the Pacific Coast, or grown in immense irrigated fields and held in reserve . . . an innovation in the Cow Country.

The range cattle business was not dead. It was only changed.

"I was purty young," Fred Garvey said, "but I remember it same as if it was yesterday. My brother died durin' it, and my pappy froze to death tryin' to get to town for the doctor. Wasn't nothin' left that spring on our place. Not a cow critter or a horse alive. Just Mamma an' me. An' she didn't live for long. Broke her heart, I guess."

9

MOST OF THE WRITING scrawled on the blackboard was indecipherable, but I could make out the names of some towns and a few figures.

It was a poolroom. When I went in I paused at the small cigar and candy counter which stood near the front door. There were three pool tables, and games were in progress at two of them. In the rear some men were playing cards, sitting at a round table like a circle of hunched owls.

An immense heavy man with a square florid face and a thick shock of gray hair covering a side of his forehead left one of the pool games and came toward me.

"Yeah?" he said.

"I was looking at the list of jobs on the board . . ."

"You want a job?"

"Well, I . . ."

"You want a job, or don't you?"

I nodded.

"All right." He stood his cue against the counter and opened a small wooden box and drew out a white file card. "Put your name down. What kind o' job? How old are you? You ain't no rider."

I felt resentment, not so much at the conclusion itself as at the blunt manner in which he uttered it. "Well, I have had some experience . . ." I began, but I stopped with the feeling that a recital of my record and capabilities would be useless. I wrote my name on the file card.

He squinted at it.

"Ever herd sheep?"

"No," I said. "And I don't think . . ."

"Ninety a month," he said.

"But I never . . ."

"Listen," he said, as if he would tolerate no argument, "take it. This is a good job. Easy. Have you got two dollars to pay for it?"

"I have two dollars," I said, "but . . ."

"All right," he said. "This man feeds good. Old Charley Gates. He needs a man right now, an' he'll treat you right. He's got to move his sheep up in the mountains right now."

"How much did you say?" I said.

"Ninety a month, I told you," he said. "He feeds good. You take the train down to Clearmont, and then the stage to Buffalo. You call up the Ness Ranch, and Charley will come for you. He might even be in town. The train goes in two hours. Here."

I took the little card he proffered. It said:

SHERIDAN EMPLOYMENT AGENCY
"Get The Best Men From Me"
Pat McClary Wyoming Poolroom

And on the back, written in ink, were the words:

OK This Man. Pat.

I gave him two dollars. He leaned over the counter toward me and his voice dropped. "Listen," he said, "there ain't no good house down in Buffalo now. I guess the sheriff was takin' too much, an' the girls pulled out on him." He had the manner of one speaking in confidence as he said, "There's two good girls right back o' this place. Just go round the corner. Second door." And he winked. "A man should have his nooky before he goes out herdin' sheep." And he gave a guttural chuckle.

I wondered if operating a poolroom and an employment agency were side lines and pimping was his true vocation.

"Thanks," I said.

I went down the street to the depot, where I had left my saddle and my bedroll, to wait for the train. I sat on a baggage truck, and I kept hearing that guttural chuckle. It gave me an unpleasant feeling in my stomach. I was glad when the train came and I could think of other things.

June had spread its magic in the Big Horns. And I thought of Brulé Kimball and Captain Winship and the slaughter of the women and children and old men. The larks probably were singing on that terrible day just as I heard them, and the foothills were breaking like great green surf against the mountain coast, just as I saw them.

We took Charley Gates' band of sheep from the North Fork of the Crazy Woman, where he had wintered and lambed them, up to the summer grazing grounds. Day after day we climbed slowly, until at last we emerged on the top of a great wall of the Big Horns.

There was Charley's summer camp, a log cabin with one window in the front, beside a narrow door. And in it were two bunks and a table and two straight chairs and an old wood-burning cookstove supported by flat rocks and a few rough shelves for utensils and groceries.

He was a rugged gaunt man with somewhat rounded shoulders and friendly blue-gray eyes that seemed always to be gazing into distance. And, indeed, most of the time they were, for from the cabin one looked down on a vast colored empire, and on days when the visibility was high one could see low blue hills beyond the Pumpkin Buttes, a hundred miles away. The range looked like a piecework quilt, the roads like lighter colored stitches twisting through it.

"I always thought it was kind o' like readin' a newspaper," he said. "Only, o' course, I know it better than you do."

But he told me how to *read* his newspaper. Horse herds traveled the fastest. Bands of sheep seemed to move scarcely at all. Trailing cattle usually were strung out like a twisting dark snake on the floor of the earth. With Charley's worn binoculars I could make out cars and wagons, going toward Kaycee or Buffalo, and I would watch them until they had disappeared in the blending colors of distance.

Charley explained the shadings by which grain and alfalfa fields could be distinguished. And one evening we saw a building burn. It appeared like a small campfire seen at a great distance.

"From the location, I'd say it was on Crockett's place," Charley said. "Poor Crockett. He's had a lot o' tough luck lately. Not long ago his wife died havin' a baby."

We watched the rain brooms sweeping the buttes and plains. The Buffalo road was flooded. We could tell that by the glint of sun on a wide mirror-like patch where ordinarily there was no water.

The sheep soon began to grow fat and contented on the rich mountain grass. They required little herding.

The lambs leaped from impulse to impulse. But the dogs held them close to the band. The dogs kept the wolves and the coyotes at safe distances, growling warnings which Charley could understand whenever the smell of a prowling animal touched their sensitive nostrils.

Day after day we climbed slowly, until at last we emerged on the top of a great wall of the Big Horns.

One evening Charley took his rifle from a wall rack, and said, "When Old Ned growls that way, it's a bear. Only it ain't very close. If it was, his tone would be a little different, like as if he was madder." He stepped out of the cabin and fired the gun in the air. "Bears won't bother us none, but they can scare the sheep." Old Ned came up to him, and he rubbed the dog's ears. "I swear he can know if a bear's anywhere in this whole dang country, even if he can't smell it."

A camptender stopped on his route once each week and left supplies and newspapers and mail and the detective magazine to which Charley was addicted. He was the only person we saw. I didn't need much in the way of personal things, but one time I asked him if he would bring me some paper and several pencils.

He made a note on his supply list. "Gonna write a book or love letters?" he said.

"Neither," I said. "Sometimes I want to write down some of the things I think about."

"I'd get arrested if I done that," he said.

The next week he brought me a large thick pad of paper that looked like it might have been made for a butcher shop.

There were days when I seemed to hear nothing at times, not even the whispering of the wind in the pines or the bird-calls or the inane bleating of the sheep.

There were nights that were deathly still. It was a stillness that seemed to make my throat tighten and my lips press together.

"Had my sheep twenty year this summer," Charley said. "Hope I can go it a few more. Towns ain't for me. Too dang much commotion. I can't sleep."

I thought: As he looks into distance, he also looks back into the years. For he saw the trail herds move into Wyoming from Kansas and Nebraska, and that wasn't long after the war had ended and the Indians were forever broken and the cavalry bugles sounded no more along the Rosebud and the Little Big Horn and the Yellowstone and the Powder.

He was a lad when he first saw Crazy Woman Creek. And he was traveling west with his father and an uncle, looking for a homestead location.

He told me about the day on which the rain fell steadily, and the two men and the boy were huddled under a tarpaulin on the seat of their wagon.

In the afternoon the curtains of water and the low gray sky made it difficult to see very far, and Uncle Ned . . . Old Ned was named in his memory and one dog was named Jeff for his father and the third dog was called Sandy simply because he was a dirty brown color . . . Uncle Ned let the lines hang loosely and the four horses found their own way across the grassy plain, splashing through pools and slipping on the harder surfaces, half-blinded by water running from the bridle straps into their eyes.

And then the wind came. At first it came in puffs, driving the rain against the tarpaulin in crackling salvos, but gradually it became steady, and at last it blew with uninterrupted fierceness.

"It'll break it up," Jeff said, and he was right. Suddenly they saw sun on a distant prairie. The sky was uncovered almost like a quilt being pulled from a bed. And clouds stood up against the horizons in strange formations, ragged temple ruins and hills and canyons and smoking fires, and the ranges sparkled with millions of diamonds.

The wind remained. And the two men and the boy having discarded the tarpaulin, clung to the wagon seat. The horses bent against the pressure, and even the wagon seemed to crouch in defiance of the great invisible force.

When they drove into a long hollow that was sheltered

by hills, the horses stopped of their own accord. Jeff said, "This is where we better stay tonight."

"There's water runnin' along the bottom back there," Uncle Ned said. "Charley, get us a bucket."

"I reckon we can get a fire goin'," Jeff said. "I'll try . . ." He stopped speaking and turned sharply about. "What was that?"

Uncle Ned said, "Sounded like somebody hurt."

"Listen," Jeff said.

"Over in that sage," Charley said.

Jeff moved quickly to take a rifle from the wagon.

"A man moved in there, I'm sure," Uncle Ned said. "I seen him."

Jeff held the rifle ready and took a few steps toward the sage. And then all three of them saw the man. He was moving in circles with small quick steps.

And Charley said to me, "I'll never forget that. Not if I live forever. When he saw us, he stopped moanin' and screamin'. He was almost naked. Just a few rags hanging on him, an' his eyes was like big black pits in his hairy face. He swung his arms just like one of them apes in the zoos. Chills me to this day."

Jeff kept his finger on the trigger of the rifle as he called out, "Who are you?"

And Uncle Ned yelled, "We don't mean no harm. Come in."

The only reply they received came in moans. And the man in the sage began to sway, as if he were keeping time to the music of some strange dance. But suddenly he stopped moving, and he stood very still with a hand cupped to an ear. And there was only the sound of the wind moaning over the sheltering hills. He seemed to be listening to it.

"Crazy as a bedbug," Uncle Ned said.

113

Jeff told Uncle Ned and Charley to remain close to the wagon as he took another step or two forward.

But suddenly the man screamed and vanished into the sage.

Jeff ran after him, shouting to him to stop. But after a few minutes he returned. And he said, "Not a sign. Gone. I think we should try to find him."

"Yes," Uncle Ned said.

"Charley," Jeff said, "you get up in the wagon and keep that other gun ready. The horses is tied good enough."

The two men started out together, walking rapidly and looking from side to side as they advanced. They made a wide circle of the hollow. And the sun was low when they abandoned the search and returned to the wagon.

In the evening the two men and the boy sat beside their campfire. The wind had died.

And each knew what the others were thinking . . . their thoughts struck fear in them and brought profound sadness.

And at last Uncle Ned said, "We ain't passed wheel track nor trail all the livin' day that I can recollect. He must have been comin' toward us, or else he didn't leave no prints. The horses woulda smelt him or seen him if he was close. He musta been comin' toward us, goin' east."

"That's the way they say the wind mostly blows in this country," Jeff said.

"The wind is crazy, too," Uncle Ned said, and got up.

Jeff and the boy stared at him.

"I think I'll just play a little before I turn in," Uncle Ned said. And he took a fiddle that was wrapped in a soft deerskin from a box in the wagon. He unwrapped it with care, as if he feared he might damage it, and he wiped the bow in the crook of his arm, and then he put the fiddle against his shoulder and bent his head over it and began to play.

Jeff and Charley sat in silence until Jeff said, "Good God,

114

Ned, that there music is sad as the moanin' wind. You'll have us crazy if you keep on."

Uncle Ned stopped and returned the fiddle to its deerskin wrapper. And then he said, "Wonder where he is now."

And in the quiet of the evenings, there on the lofty wall of the Big Horns, Charley and I read and talked and played cards.

The sheep bedded close to the cabin. The three dogs would lie just outside the open door, glancing at us now and then, as if they might be listening to our conversation or expecting some command. They were shaggy dogs, quick as foxes, obedient and intelligent. They made it possible for one man to handle a large band of sheep. A wave of an arm, and they would be off to patrol. And quite of their own accord they would drive straying animals back toward the herd. And when we moved out to graze for the day and back to the bedground for the night they would nip at the flanks of stragglers, but never doing any injury to them. And seeming never to sleep, at night they would lie on guard, their keen noses searching the stirring airs for a telltale scent of danger.

I held some thoughts that I did not disclose. Once I wished that more bears would come to annoy us. And once I imagined myself fighting alone against a pack of wolves. It was a dream that left me shaken, for in it I had failed to save the sheep, and their torn bodies were scattered over the Big Horns. And more than once I privately cursed the sheep for what they were, stupid noisy animals with running noses and the hearts of chickens, and I wished they would make trouble now and then.

I was a cleaner young man than I had ever been during my western wanderings. I spent hours washing, and pressing my clothes with an old flatiron that in some mysterious manner had found its way to Charley's summer retreat.

I was better groomed than I had been on any ranch. I

cut my hair with unnecessary frequency, using two mirrors. And quite as often I trimmed my finger and toe nails.

I constructed dams and other engineering projects in the small stream that tumbled out of the mouth of a canyon which reached far into the mountains in a narrow gorge.

I learned something about making pies and cakes and cookies from a dog-eared cookbook. But when Charley mentioned that I might be using too much flour, and remarked that not even a first-class chef could do much with the stove at hand, I abandoned my culinary pursuits.

We played cards often, but Charley preferred reading to all pastimes. I could not share this pleasure. The magazines to which he was devoted brought more disgust than entertainment. I wished that I had, after all, brought some of the books I could envision lying untouched in the den at home.

And there were times when I would suddenly realize that I had been sitting motionless, gazing into space at nothing. For I could recall seeing nothing.

One evening Charley said, "Mind if I read some of them stories you been writin'?"

"They're not really stories, I guess," I said. "Just sort of sketches . . . or something."

"Well, I'd be pleased to see them, anyway," he said, "if they ain't a private secret."

"I only have one that's really finished," I said. "It's an allegory."

"A what?" he said.

"Well, symbolic . . . That is, it's not true but it tells the truth . . . in a way," I said.

He only nodded, and I took the pages out of my bag and handed them to him. Then I went out and sat with Old Ned, because I wasn't sure I wanted to see his expressions as he read them.

This is what I had written:

In a Cheyenne saloon that was crowded with cattlemen appeared one day a quiet little man who seemed to be lost in a maze of studious thoughts. He wore a speckled tweedy suit and a large derby hat. In the opening of a soiled ironed collar bobbed a large Adam's apple. His eyes were friendly, but they seemed to be gazing far beyond the bar, perhaps even beyond the plains that surrounded the town. He took several whiskies neat, and presently fell into conversation with some of the men about him. He talked easily and in a soft voice that held the attention of his listeners. Soon there was a crowd around him, and cowmen strained to hear his words, as if mysteriously attracted by them.

"I am the greatest changer in all the plains country," the little stranger said. "Whatever a territory may be, I can change it almost overnight into something else. I am not speaking only of conditions on the surface of the earth. When I get through with a place the life in it also has changed . . . its people, its customs, its commerce, even its government. There are very few things I cannot change.

"I am as well an inventor who has contributed greatly to progress and development. I make it possible for a man to dwell in private. I can hold a man in prison, but I can also keep him out. I make it possible for a man to guard against trespassers, to isolate himself, to create his own domain, to build as he wishes. I give him protection that is not dependent upon laws or words or promises. Perhaps most important of all, I give men the power to create a country's destiny and to mold it to suit themselves."

This man must think he's God, the bartender told himself, and sent for the sheriff.

"Now, I don't do all these things for nothing," the little stranger went on. "I ask money for my services. In one way they may seem expensive, but considered in another way they are cheap. I've studied the situation in the Cattle Kingdom,

*in all the West, and I am prepared to offer a solution for its
troubles . . . at least a long step toward a solution.*

"*I am the greatest friend a homesteader ever had. But,
before you shoot me, consider also that I am the greatest friend
the cattlemen ever had. I cannot keep from helping the homesteader, but I can also help you to help yourself.*

"*There are only a few great inventors in the world, and
I am one of them. But to achieve this exalted position one also
has to be the emissary of a new age, a scientist, a businessman,
and possess the ability to make the materials of the earth serve
in new and undreamed of ways. Indeed, one must be a master
magician, but not one dealing only in illusions. One has to be
practical and precise, cold and logical. One has to upset and
destroy old standards, force old customs into discard, change
laws and traditions that have long been accepted. Change
. . ."*

*The sheriff pushed his way through the crowd. "What's
your business?"*

*The little stranger looked at him with placid eyes. "I am
the inventor of the barbed wire fence," he replied.*

Charley came to the door holding the pages in his hand.
"By golly, you know that's all right," he said. "I get it . . .
whatever you called it. But it's a good story, and danged true.
You ought to send it to this here *Western Detective* magazine.
Better'n some of the stuff it prints."

"Thanks," I said. "Maybe I will some day."

And one evening when we had finished playing cards,
Charley took up the old tally book in which he recorded our
respective gains and losses. He said, "You play good for such
a young fellow. I usually win more, even when I don't cheat."

He scribbled with a pencil in a cramped hand, and then
he said, "At a dollar a point, I figger you owe me only four

thousand, four hundred and forty-four bucks." He stared at the figures. "Kind of a funny amount, ain't it?"

And then he told me about Mr. Smart Guy. That was the name he gave him.

Mr. Smart Guy had stopped him on the street in Buffalo on a cold spring day and said, "Say, friend, could you stake a man to a meal?"

Mr. Smart Guy was dirty and thin and looked hungry. "I guess I can," Charley said. "Come in here."

He took him into the Commercial café, and he told the waitress, "Betty, I'll just have coffee and a piece of pie, but give this man a meal."

"Okeh, Charley," she said. "Hower the lambs comin' this year? Beef, pork and lamb on the dinner."

"I'll take the beef," Mr. Smart Guy said.

"Okeh," Charley said. "Good crop this year."

"That's good," she said. "Beef dinner."

"Where'd you come from?" Charley said.

"I got a ride up here from Casper," Mr. Smart Guy said, "but I live in Denver. I got a job out in Oregon, if I can get there."

"What kind o' job?" Charley said.

"A friend o' mine has a sheep ranch," Mr. Smart Guy said. "Long way without no money."

"I was just thinkin'," Charley said. "One man down to the ranch where I got my sheep was called home. It's startin' lambin' time, an' I could use another hand. Four dollars a day."

"I'll take it," Mr. Smart Guy said. "Do you think I could get credit for a jacket and a few things here?"

"That can be arranged, I think," Charley said. And when Mr. Smart Guy had finished his meal, he took him into a store, and he told the proprietor, "Mort, this man needs a warm jacket, and maybe a few socks and some underwear."

"Sure," Mort said. "I got a bargain in jackets."

The purchases amounted to twelve dollars, and Charley said, "Mort, I'd like to give you a check. Got a pencil?"

"Sure, Charley," Mort said. "Make it out for as much as you need."

Being a midwife in a lambing pen is unpleasant smelly work. Some ewes are not only stupid but are irresponsible. You pen them with the lambs they drop. And some of them want to disown their own lamb and to go their merry way, and it would die if you couldn't make its mother let it suckle. Sometimes you have to find a foster mother for an orphan. Sometimes a ewe will butt a strange lamb and kill it. Sometimes a ewe will drop twins and let only one suckle. It's not easy work, and it continues night and day. The night shifts seem endless. You have to be alert and watch for ewes that are having difficulties. And there is that incessant bawling and the smell of manure and afterbirth and dirty wet wool.

Mr. Smart Guy didn't know much about lambing, but he was, as Charley said, a "good learner," and he made himself useful, although the other men didn't like him. He was somewhat arrogant and boasted about having lived in the Brown Palace Hotel in Denver with a chorus girl from a Broadway show.

One morning he told Charley he wanted to leave, and Charley took out his little book in which he kept his labor accounts and laid it on the tailgate of a wagon, and said, "I'll give you a check. Anybody in Buffalo will cash it for you."

Then someone called to Charley from a lambing tent, and he went away for a few minutes. When he returned Mr. Smart Guy said, "I got a good pencil, if you need one."

"It's better'n mine," Charley said, as he took it. He made out the check deducting the twelve dollars which he had advanced for Mr. Smart Guy's clothes. And then he said, "You can go into town with the camptender."

"That gives me enough to ride the cushions out to Oregon," Mr. Smart Guy said.

He went into Buffalo. And the next morning he was waiting at the door of the bank when it opened. He endorsed the check and handed it to a teller.

The teller looked carefully at the signature on the check, and then he said, "How would you like it?"

"Any way," Mr. Smart Guy said. "Tens and twenties."

The teller moved as if he were going to take the money from a drawer, but he paused, and he said, "I'm sorry, but I can't cash this until Mr. Gates okehs it."

"Why not?" Mr. Smart Guy said. "I just quit workin' for him. He made it out."

"No doubt," the teller said. "But I was just curious to know when Mr. Gates learned to spell. He's been spelling forty *f-o-u-r-t-y* ever since I can recall . . . nearly twenty years. On this check it is spelled correctly."

"I'll bring him in," Mr. Smart Guy said.

"Good," the teller said. "I'll just hold the check here until you do."

Mr. Smart Guy hesitated, as if he might be going to demand the check. "Sure, okeh," he said. And he walked out of the bank.

But he never returned.

I said to Charley, "I don't understand. Did you spell forty correctly?"

"Well, probably not," Charley said. "I never saw the check I gave him again. But that ain't the point."

"I must be dumb," I said.

Without offering an opinion on that question, he said, "Later I found three blank checks missing from the back of

121

my book. I left it lyin' on the tailgate of the wagon when I was called away. He just figured he'd write a new check to himself in Buffalo, and raise it a couple hunnerd. I guess it wouldn't be hard for somebody who was good at it to imitate my scrawlin'. I never could write very good. Only he made one mistake. He knew how to spell."

"The forty," I said.

"You got it," he said.

We were playing cards that evening. I put down my hand and stepped to the door and stood looking at the stars.

Charley said, "What is it? I didn't hear nothin'."

"I thought I heard a train whistle," I said.

Charley closed the tally book and began to pick up the cards. "The railroad is a hunnerd and ten miles away, in a straight air line," he said.

"I heard it twice," I said.

I went out outside, and one of the dogs came up to me and nuzzled my leg. The moon had not risen, but its glow was visible, and there were a few clouds breaking the light. I stood very still, listening. I could hear nothing but the soft soughing of the trees.

"It's all right, son," Charley said.

I turned quickly. He was standing in the doorway, and he was smiling.

"Don't let it worry you none," he said.

"I'm sure I heard it," I said.

"Sure, you did," he said, "but in your mind and not with your ears. If you was an old sheepherder, I wouldn't think nothin' of it. They sometimes get to hearin' all kinds of things, voices and sounds that don't exist, an' there ain't nothin' to be done about it, unless they begin to forget the sheep."

"I feel foolish," I said.

He nodded, and said, "Come in."

He was sitting at the table when I went in, and in the

light of the kerosene lamp his face was marked by shadows in its deep lines.

"I'll write out your money," he said in a quiet voice, and there was a note of resignation in it, as if he not only fully understood the situation but was prepared to surrender to it. "The camptender will be comin' by tomorrow mornin', and you can go in with him."

I made an effort to quell the feeling of apprehension that had risen in me. And I said, "I'll be all right."

"Sure . . . when you get to town," he said. "I know. I was young once."

"But you'll need someone," I said.

"I reckon I can make out for a time," he said. "The camptender will get me another man to finish out the summer. Tain't long now." He handed me a check. And he said, "Raise a little hell when you get to Buffalo. There's a girl named Cloe there. She runs one o' the best places in all Wyoming. If you happen to see her, say hello for me."

10

I CAME, IN TIME, to owe a large debt to the railroads, to every one of them that crossed the West.

The coaches in which I rode, the Pullmans in which I slept, the dining cars in which I ate, were gondolas, and box-cars and reefers. And even when I had money in my pocket, I traveled in them . . . for nothing.

There were discomforts . . . cold and heat and dust and soot and undesirable companions . . . but youth aided me in enduring them. And if I had not taken advantage of this free form of transportation, I should not have got to see all the western country . . . all the magnificent immense country from Glacier National Park to the Grand Canyon, from the Colorado Rockies to the Golden Gate . . . which so greatly fascinated me and brought a restlessness which I could not control.

Often, without giving any reason, I quit a job and went into town and tossed my bedroll into an empty car of a freight train, and went wherever it was going. There was, of course, a reason, a reason that had its roots in an irresistible desire to move, to see more, to go to a place I had not seen. And there was, too, an enjoyable feeling of freedom, the luxury of being responsible only to myself, and the pleasure of unburdened nights and days.

I avoided the jungles, the places where hoboes customarily paused in their aimless journeys. I had no liking for the type of men or the companionship to be found in them. And the thought of begging brought a sensation of frustration, of helplessness, that I despised. Nor did I relish eating stew made of scraps, discarded meat and vegetables, cooked in old cans.

I could work. And I did work whenever I needed money. If I were broke . . . and I was much of the time . . . I would halt a sightseeing peregrination and get a job. I kept myself as clean as possible under the circumstances. It was not an easy thing to accomplish. But a man could, if he wanted to, get a hot bath in almost any western barbershop. And a bar of soap cost little. And water and sunshine were free. If a man were in dire need of a meal, he could usually find some means of earning it, a way to sustain himself until he could obtain more permanent employment.

Obviously I was one of the cleanest and most affluent bums who ever beat his way on western trains.

Sometimes, when I wanted to make a quick move, I would ride the blinds of a passenger train.

And there was that evening when the head and shoulders of a man suddenly rose out of the pit of darkness between the tender and the mail coach, and the whites of eyes shone in the moonlight. The Billings Express was leaving the Great Falls yards, clicking with accelerating speed over the switches along the main line.

He climbed up beside me in the shelter of the coal

126

The coaches in which I rode, the Pullmans in which I slept, the dining cars in which I ate, were gondolas, and box cars, and reefers.

bunker, and he trembled visibly and rubbed a knee. Presently he held out a thin hand, and he said, "Call me Siggie."

That was enough to tell me that he had not been long a bum. But I had also known that by his clothes and the way he spoke.

He wore Army breeches and spiral leggings, a good leather jacket and a fedora hat, and they were not very soiled. And he had an accent seldom heard on either a western freight or passenger-train blind.

Two thoughts had come quickly to me: Jews were rarely tramps. And if Siggie had had much experience bumming, he wouldn't have boarded when the train was moving so fast over a series of switches. He had been slapped hard against the side of the mail coach when he caught hold of the ladder rungs, and he was badly frightened, if not seriously hurt.

He stopped rubbing his knee, and took out a package of cigarettes. But he did not offer me one.

"This train is for Chicago?" he said.

"I guess some of the sleepers go through," I said. "They make a connection at Billings for Minneapolis and Chicago."

"Then I will be on the ocean," he said with satisfaction.

"The what?" I said. I thought that perhaps he would offer me a cigarette the next time he smoked.

He seemed to be somewhat excited as he said, "Look, is it not Chicago on the ocean? I have been through there, and I ask a man what is the water by the train, and he tells me it is the Atlantic Ocean. So I am thinking: all this way I have come from New York and I have not yet left the ocean. What a big country!"

"Big ocean, too," I said. "You've got a long ride ahead of you if you're going back to New York."

He appeared to be unimpressed by the statement. But he was obviously disturbed when he learned from me that he

131

could not travel the entire distance on the back of the same engine.

And he said, as if he were seeking to console himself, "Well, it's better than paying the money for a ticket." He spread his hands and peered intently at me. "How much it costs for a ticket! Coming out I pay it. Going back I should pay it again when I can ride for nothing?"

I laughed, and I said, "With me, it isn't a question of whether I could pay it. I'm only going to Billings, but the fact that I can beat my way is not the reason I don't ride on the cushions."

"You don't have no money?" he said, as if he were astonished.

"No," I said. "I suppose you do."

He sniffed and said, "Certainly. I got six hundred dollars. Maybe more. Who knows?"

I made no effort to conceal my disgust. His boast was an insult to both my intelligence and my experience. No one with that much money rode the blinds. And he understood that I not only did not believe him but that I was angry.

"You think I lie," he said, and smiled, as if he were amused by my incredulity. "All right, look."

He held open a wallet before me. It was filled with paper currency.

I looked away so that he would not see the extent of my consternation.

"Now," he said, and he put the wallet back in his pocket.

"Where did you get that roll?" I said, making an effort to speak with casualness.

But he must have sensed my suspicion, for he said quickly, "No, I did not steal it. You would like to know. So I will tell you. I don't lie. I make it. For nearly three months I am a bellman in Glacier Park. So, now what do you think?"

132

"If you really want to know," I said, "I think you're crazy."
"Yes?" he said.

"Yes," I said. "If you show that money on the road, some stiff will knock you on the head. Why don't you send it to New York?"

He stared at me with contemptuousness as he said, "Maybe you wouldn't understand." And quickly he held up a hand. "Don't get mad. Maybe I am wrong, see?"

His voice was apologetic as he said, "It's this way. Now I have worked all summer, and not much I spend, except for my clothes and some cigarettes, because the chef lets me eat what is left over in the kitchen. So I am telling Mamma when I come home I bring enough money so she should not worry for a while and she could have a new dress. Then she is willing I should go so far away to work."

He tapped his chest and demanded, "What is it, sending the money home with a check or some money order? Only a piece of paper with numbers on it. She won't know what it is she should do with it. A piece of paper. Now when I come home and I am saying, 'Look, Mamma, here it is! I, myself, come with the money! See, I bring it!'" And he drew a deep breath and gazed away over the moonlit rangeland. And he said, "I can hear how she will cry, even so far away. I ask you, don't a mamma like that her boy to come home with money?"

We rode for some time without talking. The train was flying downgrade, and the tender swayed, and the coaches followed like the winding glowing tail of a serpent. Red sparks passed over us and fell like a rain of fire on the mail coach. The engine purred smoothly, then roared through its stack, and fell again into a rhythmic purring. A red flare dulled the moonlight in brief flashes as the fireman opened and closed the fire door.

A vicious thought came to me, and I tried to suppress it

133

by watching the passing hills and benches. All my body seemed to be gripped by a tenseness. My own pocketbook was empty. I had eaten my last meal far back in Shelby. And there would be nothing more to eat until I reached Livingston, and then only if I could find some way to earn it.

When he tapped me on the shoulder I gave a start.

"What town is next we stop at?" he said.

"Helena," I said. Talking to him seemed to give me a feeling of relief. "That's the next big town." I explained that it was a division point, that the engine would be changed, and a new crew would take over. "We'll stay about fifteen minutes. It's not an easy place to get through. They have a railroad detective on duty."

"You have been there many times?" he said.

"I know the ropes," I said.

"You will show me?" he said.

I promised to guide him. He lighted a cigarette, apparently satisfied that he had fallen into good hands.

Suddenly the fireman came back over the coal. He looked into the water tank. Then he knelt to shield himself from the wind and smoke, and he held a lantern so he could see our faces.

"I don't care if you ride," he said, "but this engineer will make you pay. I have to tell him you're back here, because he'll ask me. If you see another light comin' over, you'll know it's him." He grinned and vanished.

Siggie stared at me with questioning eyes.

"Maybe he won't come back," I said.

But in a few minutes the engineer jumped down before us, and he asked in an unpleasant voice, "Where you going?"

"Only to Helena," I said. "We live there."

"Who do you know there?" he said.

I did not reply, knowing it would be useless. But Siggie said, "Maybe my friends you would not know." I felt like

134

laughing, and I thought it was as good an answer as any that might have been given.

"Come on, pay up," the engineer said. "A dollar apiece."

"A dollar . . . to ride here!" Siggie said, as if he were struck with amazement.

"I haven't any money," I said.

"We stop for water in a few minutes," he said. "Get off then."

When the engineer had gone, Siggie said something in Yiddish and looked helplessly at me.

"I'll show you," I said.

When the train stopped at a deserted tank station that was set in a vast moonlit prairie, we got off and walked back along the mail coach.

"We can't stay in this place," I said. "It might be two days before another train stops."

"No, no, I cannot stay here," he said.

"We'll take the blinds," I said.

We climbed up between two baggage cars. I told him to take the forward wall. It was the most protected. We stood on narrow ledges and held on to hand rails. It was a dangerous way to ride. And I warned him . . . if one dozed and slipped. "Button your jacket over the bar," I said.

He mumbled as he followed my instructions, "Never did I think of riding in such a way."

I judged that we were not more than an hour out of Helena. It was not a cold night. He looked frightened as the train started. The noise from the trucks was deafening. The wind whipped us, and cinders rained down upon us.

When the train slowed down in the Helena yards we jumped off, and I led the way to a street. We had to walk several blocks to a point in the southbound yards where I knew we could catch the train. I thought it advisable to follow a lighted thoroughfare, on which we would not be likely to attract attention. Arrest would have meant only a brief delay for me. I would have been held overnight and then sent on my way. But Siggie's money would have brought him trouble. There was little doubt that it would have disappeared.

We passed several restaurants, but Siggie did not seem to notice them. We could have waited for a freight . . . if he had offered to buy a meal. But in Livingston we would have more time, and I felt certain he would repay me for my assistance with something to eat . . . a man with six hundred dollars. Maybe more. Who knew?

He followed doggedly at my heels as we made our way through the lines of freight cars. I stopped in the shadow of a shed, and I said, "This is where she comes out. Keep out of the headlight. As soon as the engine passes we can get on. You'll have to be quick, because she will pick up speed fast. I'll take the mail coach and you get on the tender. You'll have to run fast for it. We don't want any mistakes."

"I would never have found this place without you," he said. "Lost I would have been." He stood gazing sadly along the tracks that were dotted with switch lights between shadowy lines of cars. And he said, "A friend tells me I can do it easy. On the bum he comes himself to work in Glacier Park. Cannot I do that, too, and have more money with Mamma at home?"

I felt sympathy for him, and I said, "It's not easy."

He shook his head, as if he were very weary, and he said, "It is very hard. Almost I wish sometimes I had not come."

When the train came out of the yards we flattened ourselves against the shed until the headlight had passed, and then I waved to him to go. He ran at the tender. I stepped out and swung onto the mail coach. And then I saw that he had missed the hand bar, but he had kept his footing, and he ran along the ballast, and at last he caught the bar, but instead of pulling himself up he let the train swing him. He was slapped hard against the end of the tender. But he held on. And when I dropped down beside him in the shelter of the coal bunker, he was rubbing his knee again and his eyes held a look of pain.

I started to explain the mistake he had made, but he seemed unappreciative, and I stopped. He took out his cigarettes, and I said, "Can you spare one of those?"

He broke a cigarette in two, and he said, "I divide with you. See, I give you half."

We had no trouble with the crew, and the train seldom stopped. When the fireman came back, he ignored us. It was growing light when we reached Bozeman, and the moon had long been gone, and the mountains were great dark shadows against the paling sky.

The Bozeman Tunnel, a mile and a quarter long, was ahead, and I showed him how to tie his handkerchief over his face.

He seemed terrified as he said, "The train it stops in the tunnel?"

"It won't stop," I said, "but don't forget where you are and stand up."

Then we passed swiftly into the dark entrance and I stretched out, and quickly he lay down beside me. Once, as we roared on in the complete blackness, I felt his hand touch my arm. Near the end the smoke was suffocating, and the heat from the engine was sickening. Then we shot out into the gray dawn, and I sat up and looked at him, and his face was drawn and he was shaking.

The train traveled down into the valley of the Yellowstone at a tremendous speed. It passed through the Livingston yards too fast for us to leave it. I told him to climb down on the step of the tender, and I crossed to the mail coach. I knew a level place west of the depot, and when we reached it, I let go. I landed with my feet before me and skidded along the ground to a safe stop. He fell hard, and rolled over several times. I helped him up. And in that moment I knew a strong compassion for him. He was a fool. And I pitied him.

"I think I am killed," he said, grasping for breath. "This bumming I cannot do."

But he wasn't hurt. He was only badly shaken, and he was scared.

"If I were you," I said, "I wouldn't try to take the same train out of here. A railroad dick sometimes rides in the cab to the end of the yards. Anyway, if you take my advice, you'll stay off passenger trains. Freights are easier. You can usually find an empty and get in before the train starts."

"But it will be a long wait for this freight?" he said.

"There are usually a couple in the morning," I said, "and they go fast down to Billings."

"But you do not know how soon it goes?" he said.

And again I knew the feeling of compassion. I believed he had a constant vision of his mamma's delighted face at the sight of his money.

We washed our faces and hands at a yard pump.

"I wait for the freight," he said, as if he had, after some struggle, reached a decision. "There is a restaurant here?"

"Of course," I said.

"I mean, good," he said.

"Several," I said. "Good enough, anyway."

"You will please show me?" he said.

We walked along the street to the main business section. And when we came in front of the Yellowstone Cafe, I said, "This is all right."

He moved quickly to look at a menu that was exhibited on the window. "They have the roast beef for a dollar. It is high, but I am starving. Thank you. Good-by."

And he turned in the doorway, leaving me standing on the sidewalk.

For a moment I stared after him. Then I went back along the street that paralleled the railroad. A row of cafés and small hotels and saloons faced the tracks with gloomy faces. I turned into the American Café. I had eaten there a number of times. It rated among the best of the Greek greasy spoons. And I thought, perhaps, the proprietor would remember me.

When I had finished mopping the floor and emptying spittoons, he set out a bowl of oatmeal and a stack of hot cakes and a cup of coffee. And after I had eaten, he gave me a cigarette.

The sun was bright and warm and fell like melting gold on the mountains. I walked along the street beside the railroad until I had passed the eastbound yards, and then I cut across a vacant lot to the tracks and sat down beside a pile of ties. And I fell asleep.

It was mid-morning when I awakened. I heard a road engine whistle. And when a freight came along I swung onto the ladder of a reefer. The engineer opened the throttle, as if he had been waiting until I was aboard, and the long line of refrigerators cars jerked and rapidly gained speed.

It was then I saw Siggie. I had started to climb to the top of the car, to get into the reefer box, when he came running out of a shallow culvert. He ran along the ballast, an arm extended. I waved frantically at him to stop. The train was moving too fast to be caught by anyone but an expert. And an expert would not have made the attempt.

But either he did not see me or he paid no attention to my signals. Suddenly he jumped and clutched at a ladder. Only one of his hands reached it. He was thrown violently against the side of the car. The ladder slipped from his grasp and he went down under the trucks. Almost immediately, as if he had been belched from the mouth of a cannon, he shot out. He rolled along the ballast for several feet. And then he stopped in a crumpled shapeless heap.

139

It was a foolish thing for me to do, but I crouched and let go. And I did not try to stop myself. I threw my hands over my face and tried to keep my head lowered. And when I sat up I was faint with dizziness, and my pants and shirt were badly ripped. One of my legs felt as if the skin had been torn from it. The caboose was far down the track by the time I had gathered my senses and had ascertained that my leg was not broken. I limped back to him.

He was conscious, but he could not move. I knelt beside him, and I saw that all the color had gone from his eyes. He must have been too badly hurt to feel pain, if such a thing is possible. He made no cry. But there was in his colorless eyes a look of terrible tragedy.

"I'll get a doctor quick," I said. His white lips moved slightly, and I bent close to them, and I said, "Listen, you can trust me with your money. I'll send it home for you."

I put my ear almost against his mouth to try to hear his words. But he died as he tried to speak.

I opened his jacket, and took out his wallet.

It contained only five dollars.

Then I examined some papers in it, parts of some letters and a faded photograph of a stout girl. And then I came upon a small slip of blue paper.

It was a money order receipt for six hundred and ninety dollars. The stamp of the Livingston post office was on the back of it.

11

I WAS GOING HOME THAT AUTUMN. I knew a loneliness that was accompanied by a growing distaste for the world of the bunkhouse. And these forces seemed to quell the restlessness and the urge to move on to new adventures that customarily lived in me.

I was hitch-hiking, although I had enough money to pay my fare on a train. And I seemed suddenly to have developed an intense dislike for boxcars.

An unfortunate circumstance had left me stranded in the evening on a Kansas plain. A farmer had dropped me at sunset, and I had expected to get another ride before dark, but the few cars that had passed had ignored me. For two hours I had walked along the road without reaching a settlement, and I had become resigned to spending the night in the open.

One could see a long way in that flat country. And I watched a car approaching for some time before I saw that one of its lights was very bright and the other cast only a faint gleam. I stood looking directly into the strong beam, for I wanted the driver to see my face, but I had no hope that it would stop.

But suddenly the engine died, and the car came to a slow stop only a few yards from me. I hurried toward it.

"Goin' to Emporia?" a man said.

"Yes," I said. Any haven would have been all right with me then, for I had had nothing to eat since noon.

The front door of the car swung open. "Hop in," he said. "It ain't very often I pick up anybody after dark. Not that I'm afraid."

I got in as I thanked him. He started the car with a jerk. It was an old Chevrolet sedan, and the upholstery had several rents in which the padding was exposed.

"Naw," he said, "I ain't afraid of anybody, but I just don't like ridin' with some smelly bum. If I can get a look at a man I can tell what he is almost every time."

He was small and thin, and the skin of his face was drawn tightly over his bones, and his nose was large, an arched barrier, and I wondered if it were possible for either of his eyes to see over it.

"By golly, I don't know if we'll get there or not," he said. He talked in even quiet tones that were hardly audible at times above the sound of the engine. "I got a bad tire on the rear. Liable to blow any minute."

I was about to express the hope that it would not blow when he interrupted me.

"Well, if it does," he said, "we'll be out of luck. I ain't got a thing to fix it with. I suppose it was foolish to start out this way. It's all of seventy-five miles."

I said nothing, and he went on, "Yeah, I'm glad, too, it ain't cold. I figger to drive about twenty. That will put us there about midnight, if she holds out. Don't dare go no faster. This gravel is hard on rubber, and there's some bad places. I know this road like a book. Been over it ten or twenty times, I bet, in the last two years. Come far?"

"From New Mexico," I said.

"All the way down there, eh?" he said. "Well, I know that country. Ain't a foot I don't know. I put in a good many years down there along the border and below. I was with Pershing's outfit the first time I was down. Drivin' a truck. That's what started me on the road to hell, Mexico an' the greasers.

"I only been in Wichita about three months this time. Course, I been around Emporia a lot. Tulsa, too. And Oklahoma City. I got a sister in Wichita. She works in one o' these beauty parlors. Makes good money, too. I was stayin' with her, but we had a row today, so I just packed up an' pulled out. I ain't one to fight with a woman. Not me. You can't get no place. We was arguin' about two weeks now, an' I finally got a bellyful.

"Maybe I should of stayed, though. Startin' out broke an' with a bum tire. That's crazy. I know I get hot easy, but it's too late to go back now."

I did not inquire the reason for the argument, but as if he anticipated the question, he said, "Oh, we was just fightin' over a business proposition of mine. She was goin' to finance a scheme I had, an' then after we got started, an' had some printin' done, then she don't want to do nothin' more. I guess that's what you can expect from a woman. A man gets disgusted. If he's got to deal with a woman, he might as well quit. He just ought to take a gun an' end it all. I got me a gun, too, an' today I was so mad I felt like usin' it. Goin' far?"

"Chicago," I said.

"Old Chi, eh?" he said. "That's a good town. I know Chi. Do you know where State Street is?"

"Yes," I said. "In the Loop."

"Madison and State?" he said.

"Yes," I said.

"They call that the busiest corner in the world," he said. "Well, maybe. But there's a corner in Wichita I bet's as busy. They counted the cars there once. I don't remember the figger, but it was one or two hunnerd. Maybe more. Madison and State ain't no busier. But it's a great town, old Chi. I ain't been there for more'n ten year, an' maybe I wouldn't know it no more.

"I come out here after the war, because I thought maybe the climate would help me. Got all bunged up in France. That's why I am what I am. A wreck. You might not think it to look at me, but I've spent more'n six year altogether in hospitals. Don't seem I can stay out of one very long. I just sort o' lose my ambition. Sort of give out evry now and then.

"That's why I can't hold no job. Soon as I get one an' work a while, I get down again. It just don't seem I can make nothin' go. An' I get plenty of good ideas, too. I know they're good.

"That's what I was doin' in Wichita, workin' out a scheme I had. I swear, I get all burned up when I think about it. Just makes a guy want to shoot himself. Yeah, bump off."

I wondered if I could be sympathetic or encouraging in some way, but before I had said anything, he said, "Now, here's what I was doin'. I had some Mexican jumpin' beans. Ever see 'em?"

"Yes," I said.

"All right," he said. "Well, maybe you don't know they gamble with 'em down in Mexico. So I got up a game. I worked for a whole week or more diggin' up some Indian symbols and workin' out a design. You see, each one means somethin' in Indian, an' it would score so much. It's a little like fortune tellin', only it ain't. I put these here symbols down on cardboard, each one in a space, an' I worked out rules. You move the beans around the cardboard by shakin' dice. Maybe

144

they jump, an' if they do, it counts somethin', or maybe you lose somethin'. Everything counts, whether they jump or not.

"I showed it to my sister, an' she was nuts about it, an' said she'd finance it. Well, we got a thousand printed up for a start. Then she loses interest. Can you imagine?

"I had to have money to get envelopes printed and to buy a lot o' beans with, an' they only jump up to October, I think it is. Then they rest for the winter, or somethin'. So I had to hurry, or wait till next spring. Then she says we better wait till next year when the beans begin jumpin' again, an' we'd sell a lot.

"I got the thousand cards in the back o' the car with me. You bet I didn't leave 'em.

"I laid around two months tryin' to get her to do somethin', but she wouldn't. She just played like she was deaf. Finally I got sore. Then she blew up.

"That's just the way it goes with everything I touch. But a man can fight only so long, an' when he keeps on gettin' licked he better retreat. Just take him a gun an' . . ."

"Everything can't always go that way," I said.

"Well, that's what a man would think," he said. "The other day I was thinkin' maybe if I went back down to Mexico I'd be better off. Mexico City, that's a good town. I hear they got a good hospital there.

"Remember when Pershing, old Black Jack, went down there after bandits? Well, I went right along. You couldn't keep me out of a fuss when I was okeh. I'd been workin' around the border, even clear down to Tampico, then. Columbus, New Mexico, that's where some of the trouble started. Ain't much of a place. Wouldn't nobody have ever heard of it to this day, I guess, if Villa hadn't come over an' shot it up.

"I tell you that whole country along the border is a tough one. A white man ain't got a chance. I remember once down in Cruces, I got in there broke, an' I met a tank builder

145

in a saloon. Him an' me sort o' took to each other, an' he offered me some work. He had a couple o' tanks to build.

"Well, we went to work, an' he had a Mexican helpin' him before I come along, an' this Mex was sore because he hired me an' not him. He whined all over town that he was goin' to get me for stealin' his job. Hell, this was in my own country, wasn't it? If it had been in Mexico, it might have been different.

"Well, we got through with the tanks on a Saturday night, an' we went down to the saloon an' got drunk. Here was this Mex, an' he was drunk, too. He got in front o' me an' said he was goin' to cut my throat. So I just turned myself loose on him.

"Well, I got pinched an' thrown in the jug. You know Cruces was all Mex in those days, even though it was in this country. The greasers was the law, an' they treated white men the way they wanted to. There was six of 'em in the jail with me, an' they didn't like the idea of havin' an American in with 'em. I could speak the lingo some, an' I made out they was talkin' about mobbin' me. So I climbed up on top of a cell that stuck out from a corner, an' lay down. I found an empty beer bottle up there. So I took off one o' my socks an' put the bottle in it. I was ready for 'em. The first one to show his head over the edge o' that cell would get a beer bottle broke on it.

"Well, purty soon in come a Filipino. I don't know where they got him, but there he was. The greasers was all whisperin' together about him, an' I guess he didn't like their looks neither, so he climbed up with me. But then he started in cussin' the United States an' the Army an' the Navy . . . I guess he had been on a battleship, like maybe a dishwasher or a slop boy or somethin' . . . an' I got tired o' listenin'. I didn't wait to use the bottle. I just used my fist, an' knocked

146

I looked at the tire. It was almost torn from the wheel. And then I gathered some twigs and started a fire.

him in a loop off the cell. He stayed where he landed, out cold, an' after that the greasers cut out their whisperin'.

"So, about daylight a turnkey come in an' told me I'd have to go out an' sweep the street. I didn't like the idea, but I thought I might get a chance to beat it, so I went along quiet. Outside he give me a big wire brush with a long handle an' said he'd show me where to begin.

"Well, he took me across the street in front of a saloon. Some cowboys was there waitin' for the place to open, I guess, an' they was Americans. The Mex turnkey got a kick out o' that, makin' me work in front o' my own kind. I begun to push the brush a little, an' he sort o' turned away grinnin' so the cowboys could see him. All at once I said somethin', an' when he turned I stuck that wire brush right in his face as hard as I could. You should of heard him yell. As if I'd murdered him. The blood just squirted out of his face in a dozen little streams, an' he couldn't see for it in his eyes. Maybe he never saw good after that, but I wouldn't know.

"I beat it. Nobody tried to stop me. I didn't expect them American cowboys would. So I got away. I lit right out across the desert.

"You won't believe me when I tell you I walked forty miles with only one or two drinks o' water. Along late in the second night I seen a campfire, an' I headed for it. I couldn't make a sound, my tongue was so swelled up, an' I was weavin' like a drunk.

"There was a bunch o' deserters in the camp from the Mexican Army. You know evry time Mexican troops got near the border, some would desert an' come across. The same was true of Villa's bunch. They would all head for a certain ranch. The Mex who owned it was rich, an' he didn't like the Mexican Government or the politicians, or somethin', so all deserters was welcome on his place.

"Well, they give me some wine an' a little water, an'

151

later on some food. They know how to treat a man lost in the desert.

"The next morning the rancher himself come ridin' into camp. I remember him well. He was a big fine-lookin' Mex who owned a lot o' range this side o' the line, an' he had silver all over his saddle. He asked me some questions, an' then he give me five bucks an' told me to walk twelve miles to a road that would take me to an American ranch. I took a bottle o' water an' some tortillas, or somethin', an' started out. That night I stayed at an American ranch that was right on the border. I never went back to Cruces since.

"Say, the stars is bright tonight. Nice time o' year here in Kansas. But winter's comin', an' the snow. Winter gets a man down. That's one thing I like about Mexico. The winter is good. But I don't think I'll ever see it no more. I can't go very far from the governmint hospital here without money to pay for treatments. That's one reason I wanted to work out this jumpin' bean scheme. I would have some money in my pocket extra.

"Look at this old buggy, too. I paid a hunnerd dollars for it two year ago in K.C., an' I ain't spent a dime for repairs, but it needs work on it now, an' me with nineteen cents.

"I got some friends in Emporia, but won't nobody loan me more'n a dollar. They think I'm liable to bump off any minute, an' maybe I am. You can't make a dead man pay back what he owed."

"Did you see any fighting when you were with Pershing?" I said.

"What there was," he said. "When I come back, I enlisted again, even though I had swore I was through with the Army forever. France is where I seen the fightin'. That was real . . . Damn! There she goes! We only come less than fifty miles, too. An' that tire can't be fixed. There's six patches on it now.

"Well, hell, I'll pull up under that tree. We can build a fire."

I looked at the tire. It was almost torn from the wheel. And then I gathered some twigs and started a fire.

"Feels good," he said. "I wish we had somethin' to eat. Maybe somebody will give us a lift in the morning. I got to raise some money some way in Emporia, but I don't know how I will, unless . . ."

He took a revolver from his pocket.

"Maybe I can sell it," he said. "It's a good gun. Thirty-eight. Maybe I could borrow a couple o' bucks on it. I'd like to keep it, because . . ."

"Must be a town ahead," I said. "There are some lights . . . Maybe you could get a secondhand tire there."

He stared at the gun, turning it over in his hand, as he said, "If I had the price. They don't give 'em away." He dropped down beside the little fire. "Broke . . . a flat . . . hungry . . . all bunged up inside . . . What's the use? Instead o' sellin' the gun, I better use it. Why not? I ain't afraid. I seen better men than me do it in France when they was shellshocked or had got some disease they was ashamed to go home with. Died in battle, the reports said. I know better."

I stood over him, and I said, "Will you take five dollars for it?"

He looked incredulously up at me: "For what?" he said.

"For the gun," I said. "You can get a secondhand tire for that."

I held out the bill, and he took it, and he turned it over several times as he looked at it, and then he handed me the gun.

"Ain't got no bullets for it," he said.

I turned away, more confused than angered. But he could get bullets, I thought, and then I was glad that I had bought it. And I said, "Look, why don't you get in the car and sleep until morning? I have to go on."

"What's the hurry?" he said, as if he did not want me to go.

"Well, I have to get along," I said. "So long. Good luck."

I walked rapidly along the dark road. And after I had gone a short distance, I threw the gun into a field.

12

ARRIVED IN ELKO IN A BOXCAR. But I had some money, for I had worked three months on a ranch in the Sierra foothills, over in California. I got a room at the Commercial Hotel and bathed and shaved and put on clean clothes.

It was this way there in Elko on that spring evening: a lingering sun on the Ruby Mountains, and the quiet of the big country making itself felt in the town, and lights beginning to show in the little shacks, and a road engine purring over beyond the depot, waiting to hook on to the Limited. The saloons were quiet. There were few games going. And the men slumped along the bars as if they didn't want any uproar.

This fellow I met, Tuck, said he'd had his supper and he was going across the tracks to see a girl he knew. And I thought I would go out to the airport . . . it was only a few blocks away . . . to watch the Salt Lake mail plane come in. That was something to see, a mail plane. They were little open-cockpit machines in those days, and as the saying went, the men who handled the stick flew by God and the seat of their pants. There were few lights and fewer weather reports and it was terribly cold going over the mountains. You had to admire the pilots in their fur-lined suits, they were heroes.

"This girl just came here a few days ago," Tuck said. "I ran into her over at the post office and I said I'd see her."

"You don't have to explain to me," I said.

"We used to be good friends," he said.

"Why not?" I said.

"I don't know," he said. "I didn't know she was in town."

When I came back from the airport I went into the Commercial House and got something to eat, and then I went into the bar. Another fellow I had met named Alabama was there in a game with brown chips, and that was big stakes even in Elko.

There was a crowd watching. I got through it close enough to see the table over a railroad man's shoulder. There were two Chinese in the game and whenever they played there was an audience. But they weren't any better than the Italian, only they were more interesting to watch. The little Chinese owned a couple of laundries and the fat one ran the Eagle Cafe and the way his pudgy fingers handled the cards and chips made me uneasy. They were stubby but they dealt the cards like running water and they made the chips slip down like round smooth petals falling. The faces of the Chinese were like creased yellow rock and in between them Alabama's face looked long and sad and dark. A cowman sat next to the houseman, and he was steamed with liquor so that he slumped a little to one side. And he was losing steadily. With brown chips in the game, the houseman broke open a new deck every few hands and threw the old deck on the floor behind him.

The two cowboys pushed their way through the crowd and stood behind the cowman's chair until a hand ended. And then one of them tapped him on the shoulder and said, "Cash in."

"Come on, get out," the other said.

The cowman said, "Let me alone."

"We want something left," one of the cowboys said.

And they pulled the cowman from his chair and pushed him out through the crowd.

I saw Tuck come in, but he went upstairs in the hotel without looking at anyone. I went over to the bar and got a drink. And then I went outside. I wanted to get the smell of the saloon out of my nose. And I walked out to the end of a street and smelled the fresh night air of the desert.

There were a lot of cowboys in Elko the next morning. They had come down from the Ruby country to take some cattle back. Nearly two hundred cars had unloaded.

I slept late and while I was eating my breakfast Tuck sat down beside me. He told me the telephone company wanted linemen. He'd gone over to the office that morning and had got a job. I knew about it, for I'd read in the paper about the new line to be built, but I couldn't make up my mind about applying. I thought I might go to work for one of the cow outfits up near Oregon. But Tuck kept on talking up the telephone company. And at last I said I would go to see them. He made it sound better than working on a ranch all summer.

There was deep snow on the Ruby Mountains and the Humboldt River was high and the night air had the feel of frost, but there were bright green patches on the red south slopes where the range grass was breaking through and in places small yellow flowers cuddled the warming earth. It made you think of getting started at something.

After I had eaten, Tuck and I went outside and sat on the curb by the side of the hotel. There was a small sign in the bank building right across the street that kept flicking on and off.

$1.00 OPENS A SAVINGS ACCOUNT

"That's what you better do," Tuck said.

"What?" I said.

"Open a savings account," he said. "The telephone company man didn't seem to like it because I didn't have one."

"With a dollar?" I said.

"They won't know how much you got in it," he said.

"I hate to tie up a dollar like that," I said.

The bank was tan stone, four stories high, and it stood up like a big tree in a jumble of kindling wood. It was the only tall modern building in Elko, except the hotel, and that was only three stories high. The bank made you realize that a new age was coming, even in such a place as Elko. The thought didn't rest well with me. And I didn't like to think of myself going in and tossing a dollar on the marble counter. If it wouldn't have mattered to the telephone company, I would rather have given it to the bartender in the Commercial House to keep for me.

The bank building had an elevator in it that resembled a big moving bird cage. It was the only elevator between Ogden and Reno. A young girl in a tan uniform operated it. And she tried to maintain an air of detachment, but she didn't quite achieve it. Presently some cowboys with nothing else to do sat down on the curb near us. And they seemed to be fascinated by the sight of the girl going up and down in the bird cage.

"They want college boys, if they can get them," Tuck said. "I guess they want to make linemen out of professors. But there's damn few college boys hangin' around this burg."

"I graduated from Harvard and Oxford," I said. "Then I went to Yale to finish up."

158

"Funny I never saw you there," he said. "They want go-getters with manners, too, who go to church regular and write home every day. That's why I got the job."

"I'm as good as hired," I said.

"Maybe I'll see you tonight," he said. "We might go across the tracks. I know a couple of girls."

"I have to hang on to my money," I said.

"You don't need to spend any," he said.

The telephone station had a white picket fence around it and a green lawn in front that was afflicted with pockmarks of bare red clay. The cables dipped down from the poles and ran in one side of the building and out the other side. And they made me think of lines running clear across the country like that, every now and then dipping down to keep in touch with the earth, unloading the confused voices of all the people who were crying out to each other and trying to straighten out the mess they had made of their lives.

The young man with whom I spoke wore a starched gray shirt and his black tie was precise and his hair was slicked down in fine inked lines. Everything on his desk was in order. Even the pencils were laid together in an even row. And at a glance you knew that each wire in the place ran right into the very hole intended for it, and the rows of black and red buttons on the switchboards were in perfect lines, and each impulse was premeditated, and if there was disorder in the world beyond the door none would be tolerated in this immaculate realm.

But while the young man talked to me, I had difficulty in keeping my eyes from a tiny crumpled piece of blue paper someone must have dropped inadvertently on the polished linoleum floor.

"We give you a course in line construction first," he said in a way that made me think he had studied and practiced his speech, "then you go out to the camp. We want only young men of good character, you know, good intelligence, go-getters who want a future, stickers looking for promotion. It's waiting. The company is expanding. Who sent you?"

All the time he was reciting, I continued to glance at the little piece of blue paper. And I wondered how it alone could so greatly upset the ingenious perfection of the place.

"I came all the way from Salt Lake to get this job," I said.

Then I knew he was going to hire me. And I regretted going there. I felt as if something were going to be taken away from me, something I didn't want to lose.

"The company wants to see what a man has in his head before they trust him to work on a telephone line that will cost millions to build," he said. "Here are your examinations. Sit down and fill them out."

It was dusk when I went into the Commercial House bar. I was looking for Tuck. Alabama motioned to me to join him. His voice was cordial as he said, "Hello there, friend. Get it?"

"Get what?" I said.

"The job," he said. "I saw you come out just before I went in. It's come to the point where I have no choice."

"Get taken last night?" I said.

"I did very well for a time," he said. "It was that Chink. Crafty devil. Too bad a man has to play with such people. Oh, well . . . A drink on me, sir, now we'll be workin' together. You don't look like a telephone lineman. Maybe I don't. No offense, sir. I see you in a saddle, not on a pole."

"You got it all figured out, haven't you?" I said.

"Gambler's way, I expect," he said. "Always gambled. My pappy taught me, and Baton Rouge never knew no better than him, sir. But I'm a trained lawyer, too. Yes, sir, Alabama University. You didn't suspect that. Mighty fine school. Gentleman's school. You see how it is. You're a rider, and now you're a lineman. Well, I'm a lawyer. That's the way of things.

160

It isn't what you have been, it's what you are this very moment at hand that shapes your destiny. Yes, sir."

I wanted to get away from Alabama. And I wondered where Tuck was. I bought him a drink, and left. It was dark, and I walked along the street and stepped right from pavement into desert. That was the way it was then in Elko. The town was closely woven, and you were either in it or in the desert. I sat down on a rock. And a horseman came along the gravel road. He slumped in his saddle, as if he were tired. He came out of starry space and rode into town along the side of the paving, the little horse by choice keeping to the narrow dirt shoulder.

And I thought: The little horse is thinking of the livery barn ahead in the confusion of shacks and of the annoying odors it holds of strange horses mysteriously gone. The little horse would have more peace of mind when it left concrete once more, when it turned outward again, the desert under foot, the familiar fragrance in its nostrils, the sounds it understood touching its ears.

And I wondered again if I wanted the telephone company job. The new line would bring all the world closer to Elko . . . to a thousand little towns like it . . . pressing down upon it, helping to destroy the alliance of bigness and emptiness, to conquer them. And I wondered if I wanted to spend my time helping to do that.

I went back, and I found Tuck in the Commercial bar, and we went across the tracks to the older part of town, to the streets lined with squatty Mexican houses, small cheap hotels and gambling joints. They symbolized the Elko that was fading away. And along the old main street the buildings had high false fronts, some of them with names still visible on them . . . Stampede and Last Chance and Gold Nugget. Gunmen remained, but their guns were concealed, hidden somewhere. Dealers were there, but the fancy vests were gone.

Bare incandescent bulbs glowed where coal oil lamps had flickered. The old bars, solid and polished, looked forlorn, funereal. The best buildings were the whorehouses. They had a business that didn't change with time. They were inviting buildings, painted and neat.

We went into the Four Leaf Clover. Tuck said he knew the girls there. But he knew only one. And I had suspected that was the case. Her name was Doris. And he had known her when he was riding for an outfit with headquarters in Winnemucca.

We had to spend something, so we bought cigars and dropped nickels in the piano. It was a high-class place. Nobody pressured you.

Doris sat on a couch between us. She put an arm around Tuck, and he looked unhappy. She asked Tuck if he wanted to dance, but he only laughed and looked embarrassed, as if he didn't understand the language. She had bright dark eyes, not faded like the eyes of most girls in such places. She took my arm.

"Let's dance," she said.

Her hair was fresh and smooth and dark, and she smelled good, and she was soft up against me. It would have been a pleasure to have gone to bed with her, but I dismissed the thought. I could see how much she liked Tuck, and I had the feeling that he liked her more than he was revealing. Perhaps he wouldn't have cared if I had gone with her. We were good friends. But I didn't. And I didn't like the looks of the other two girls who were there.

She got Tuck to dance. And I sat watching them. And she kept talking to him, but he seemed to be looking into distance, and I wondered if he actually heard what she was saying. He had sweat on his forehead when they sat down. She kept her arm linked in his arm. Their silence made me uncomfortable. And I had the impression that she wished he

162

would go with her to her room. I never knew why he didn't go. It wouldn't have cost him anything. But it was none of my business, and I said nothing about it.

I knew she was trying not to look at the big cowboy who came in. But he saw her at once. And he came across the room toward her. He'd had a little more liquor than he could comfortably carry, but he was pleasant enough.

"Hello, sweetheart," he said. And he took her hand and pulled her up.

She said to Tuck, "Don't go. I'll be back in a minute."

Tuck didn't look at her.

"Will you wait?" she said.

"All right," he said.

But when they had gone through the door at the other end of the room, he got up, and he said, "Let's get out o' here."

"You told her you'd wait," I said.

"Why should I?" he said.

And we went out, and we had gotten almost back across the tracks before he spoke again. And then I believed I knew why he had wanted me to go with him.

"What would you do?" he said.

"I'm not sure," I said. "She's nice."

"A man can't tie to a girl like her," he said. "She used to be that way down in Winnemucca. I hate to hurt her. I was sorry when I run into her here. Do you get me?"

"Yes," I said.

The telephone company put up a wooden building for the training school near the Commercial Hotel. The instructor's name was McCleary. He was a friendly little man, always sober, and he had a nipper manner which must have come from years of climbing poles and stringing wires. His efficiency had got him the job, no doubt, and I had the feeling that he was well qualified to teach the class of thirty greenhorns how to build a line costing millions. He owned a neat

163

bungalow out in California, overlooking San Francisco Bay, and one day he showed us pictures of it. He had brought his wife and daughter with him, and he ate his meals with them in the Commercial café, but he never introduced us to them.

He drove us with a wearing persistence, seeming never to think of rest during the eight hours we went to school each day. The building had rough wooden benches and tables. At one time we worked several days on a course in first aid, and one fellow mumbled that he thought we had been tricked into preparing for war.

"When do we start target practice?" George said. "And get our bayonets?"

McCleary laughed, and said, "You may think it's war when ice takes a line down some night, or a brush fire cracks off the poles like matches, or when men fall off thirty-foot cross-arms."

We learned to make splints for broken limbs, and we learned how to treat sunstroke, snakebite, frostbite, colds, hernias, bruises and burns.

"What about misery?" Alabama said.

"You'll learn about that from experience," McCleary said in a way that made me think he didn't care much for Alabama. He rubbed his thin nimble hands together. "You're all doing fine," he said. "I can send in a good report. Study your handbooks tonight. Safety is paramount, paramount, but you got to know the work. Study that wire splicing. You'll get it."

Alabama was always the first to the bar at five o'clock, when we were dismissed for the day. And he said one afternoon, "Dry stuff in there. Dry as that there desert."

"Luck," I said as I took a drink of beer.

"Thank you much, sir," he said. "I wish the same to you. I certainly do. A man has to be careful who he takes up with in a country like this, and between you an' me, sir, I'm a particular man."

164

We got our spikes. McCleary showed us how to climb. He moved up and down the poles back of the school building like a walking frog. And at the top, he leaned out and twisted in his safety belt to demonstrate the needlessness of fear. He drew up a cross-arm that was longer than himself, and almost as heavy, and juggled it into place. And he drove spikes and set braces at all angles.

Some of us got up ten feet the first day. And then most of us shook and slid down, burning our hands and legs. The next day we all got to the top, except George, and he only went halfway when he began to shake and let go. He slid all the way down, driving splinters into his arms and legs. He was big and heavy, and he flushed, but you could see he was more angry than ashamed.

The kid named Herson ran up and down the poles like a monkey and did acrobatic stunts on the top.

"Natural ability," McCleary said. "Any man who can climb like that on his second day is a natural." Then he yelled up to Herson, "Come down before you get too smart and break your neck."

George was at the bar that evening when I went in, and for the first time he began to talk to me and bought me a drink.

"You climb all right," he said.

"I got burnt, too," I said.

"I'll be on fire by tomorrow," he said. "That little weasel, Herson, showing off makes me sick."

"Forget him," I said.

"Will you come out along the road with me?" he said. "I got a Ford."

We drove out to where the mainline poles skirted the highway and the railroad. George put on spikes and belt and began to climb. But he didn't get far when he came slowly down. His face was wet with sweat and he looked scared.

"You'll make it," I said.

"I'll make a corpse," he said.

"Look," I said, "what did you do before?"

"I was only a cowpunch," he said. "You think I'm yellow."

"No, I don't think any such thing," I said.

"The old lady made me quit ridin'," he said. "I was good with broncs, and I could make good money breakin' 'em, but she thought it was too dangerous. I got me a homestead over here near Winnemucca, an' it looks like I'm goin' back to it, but I can't make a livin' on it."

"That's it, then," I said.

"What's it?" he said.

"Who's going to take care of her, if you get it?" I said.

"Maybe," he said.

"Don't you know you're insured on this job?" I said. "If you get it, she'll get more than you can make for her. Even if you only get laid up for a time, you get some pay. All this first-aid stuff and talk about danger has got you worried."

"That scissor-built McCleary don't tell a man nothin'," he said.

And he spit on his hands and he went up high on the pole. He nearly slipped out, and he lost his hat, but he didn't fall. And then a car came up and stopped and McCleary got out. He had his wife and daughter with him. And he stood staring up at George in amazement. George just stayed on the pole. And McCleary got back in his car without saying a word and drove away.

George came down, and he said, "I guess I'll get hell."

"I'd bet you a drink you're wrong," I said.

"Maybe we ain't insured out here, after five o'clock," he said.

Then the day came when we were loaded into a big truck. And we bobbed along the yellow highway, through the big hills east of Elko. After an hour or so we turned into a rutted

166

road that ran along a high ridge above a valley. The sun was hot, and there were larks singing, and the Ruby Mountains held silvery peaks right against a lilac sky.

We crossed over the ridge and dipped down into another valley, and the tracks of the road were two threads winding across its floor. It was a long way back in thought to the Commercial bar and the Four Leaf Clover, for this was the world as it was made by nature, not by man, this was the world in which you came to know the alliance of bigness and emptiness.

We came eventually to the railroad, and the truck stopped beside an old passenger coach which was the camp office. A short distance away was a mess car and two other cars with double-decked bunks built into them. And there was a fine old car that was fixed up as a recreation room. It contained a few tables and chairs and a phonograph. It had been a club car, and the fine panels were still glossy in places, and at one end there were two heavy pillars that looked like mahogany. Someone had carved initials in one of the pillars. Next to the mess car were several boxcars that were used for supplies and tools and materials.

A score of men had been there several days, digging holes and hauling poles. It was just after noon when we arrived, and they were already eating when we joined them. The cooks were Chinese, and they chattered like a bunch of parrots while they were putting the meal on the table for us. It was hot in the mess car, and some of the men ate without their shirts, but the heat didn't seem to affect their appetites.

The camp foreman was Mallory. He was almost square from the shoulders down, and his hair was a coppery brown that glinted in the sun. He called us together after we had eaten. And he spoke to us in such a soft voice that it was difficult to hear him.

"It's serious business," he said, "and this section will be

167

hell. It's almost solid rock in places, and they won't send us no powder. Post holes are better dug than blown out. We only got about four months to work altogether, and we can't make mistakes. It will be too cold after that, and then we'll go out to Oregon. The engineers will be ready for us out there then, and we can work all winter. It rains most o' the time out in that coast country, but it's better than forty below." He swung around and thumped a man on the shoulder with a beefy palm. And he said, "All right, let's get at it."

That summer the heat was brutal at times. And the sun was blinding and it seemed to smelt the sand and rock together. Sweat dried in a crust on your body. And on some days the wind blew wildly and stirred up a smoke dust, making your mouth leather that water could not soften.

The new pole holes dotted the parched flats as if a peg-leg giant had marched across them. And hammering on rock all day with an iron bar you felt trapped by a monotonous rhythm, a rhythm that seemed born of distance, each beat striking at you and fading into the eternity beyond. The peeled poles stood up at crazy angles until the setters and tampers came along. A truck let wires out behind it, thin streams of steel water catching the sun darts. Then we hung over cross-arms like men cruified in ridiculous positions, tying, spiking, bolting. At last the new line stood like a great picket fence enclosing the earth.

One afternoon I was sent back along a section of finished line to gather nuts and bolts and anything else that was worth salvaging. I piled whatever I picked up at the foot of each pole, where they could be found easily and taken into camp at a later time. The country seemed to be more immense than it had before, probably because I was alone in it. I crossed a flat beyond some low yellow hills, and a half-circle of red peaks stood up ahead, and the ground was covered thickly with dull green sage and blue cactus. I looked for something

168

moving, but there were only dead bare rocks burning in the afternoon sun, sand and sage and cactus and white washes and promontories that looked as if they were smeared with dried blood. Only the orange heat waves moved.

The line crossed the highway. I could recall digging the hole for one of the fifty-foot poles that lifted the wires there. A buzzard was sitting on top of that pole. I threw a rock at it.

And then a car came up suddenly beside me and stopped. And Doris leaned out, and she was smiling.

"What do you say?" she said. "Don't you know me?"

"Sure," I said. "What are you doing way out here?"

"Taking a drive," she said. She was wearing a fluffy orange dress which seemed to make her eyes blacker and her skin the color of peaches. "Where's Tuck?"

"I think he's out the other way today," I said. "Where'd you get the swell car?"

"What do you think?" she said. "It's mine. Eighteen hundred flat, and I paid it. Get in."

"I'm working," I said.

"Get in," she said. "You can take five for a smoke."

I leaned on the car door, and I said, "If you want to see Tuck, you'll have to go back along the wagon road along the tracks."

"Who said I wanted to see him?" she said. "Did he get my letters?"

"How would I know?" I said.

"You might," she said.

"I'm not the postman," I said.

"Don't get me wrong," she said. "It's my day off."

"Well, tell me why you came out here, then," I said.

"You're a funny guy," she said.

I could smell her perfume, and out there it seemed to smell better than it had in the Four Leaf Clover.

"All right," she said. "Why don't he write to me? He's

169

a damn fool. I told him what I'd do. I have a good roll in the bank, and I've got a chance like I never had before. There's an old cowhunky from up north some place after Suzie. He wants her to sell out. What a chance for her! I hear he's got a good outfit."

"Maybe she don't want it," I said.

"She wants it," she said. "She's got him sewed up. She'd kill any other girl that looked at him."

"Well?" I said.

"Just this," she said. "She's going to sell out and marry the old buzzard. And who to? Me. I got an option. She's willing to take two installments in a year. It's easy. That's the best house in town, the Four Leaf Clover, and you know it is."

"What do you want me to do?" I said. "Ask Tuck?"

Her lips twisted, as if in bitterness, and she said, "You can mind your own business."

"Okeh," I said, and I stepped back, and she started the motor and turned the car around, and then she let it die again and leaned out and looked at me. And she said, "You can find out if he got my letters, if you want to."

"What if he did?" I said.

"Well, nothing, I guess," she said. "Just say hello to him for me."

A few days later the kid, Herson, was working on the same pole with me, and he slipped when he was thirty-five feet up. I tried to get him, but his shirt tore through my fingers. And he went down, kicking like a madman at the pole with his spikes. But he only caught the air. And he bashed his head and took the flesh off the inside of his arms. His face was covered with blood. They carried him on a stretcher to a truck. And then I got sick inside and the earth began to tilt and a red rain began to fall. I knew I had a brace, because I could feel the iron cutting into an armpit, but I

*A buzzard was sitting on top of that pole. I
threw a rock at it.*

couldn't see, and I knew one of my spikes had broken out, and I couldn't find wood for it.

They said George went up that pole like a swearing baboon, and they said he brought me down like I was a little boy. And then I knew that I hadn't felt the brace at all. It was his arm around me.

"You picked a hell of a place to go out," Mallory said in his soft voice. "You ought to have more consideration for us."

The earphones took you right back into the world. Eastward the line talked, westward was the stillness, only the wind stirring sage and grass. When the orchestra stopped playing a girl asked me who I was, and when I told her she laughed, and she said, "How's for a dance, baby? Up on the pole."

"See you tonight," I said.

And then she was gone, into the great silence.

"How is it out there?" a man said.

"Hotter than hell and a dust storm coming," some other man said.

"That Boston baby is sure dumb," the Salt Lake operator said.

The Ruby Mountains were lost in dust, and the sky looked like dark coffee grounds. I wished I could tell the dumb Boston baby about it, but the Salt Lake operator had cut us off. Maybe she wouldn't have been so dumb if she had known what her voice was going through.

And this evening Alabama asked if he might talk in confidence with me, and we walked down the tracks a way. But I didn't listen long to what he had to say.

"Just keep away from me," I said, and I turned back. He persisted in talking and walking along with me. And suddenly I hit him and knocked him down. But he got up quickly and he showed that he knew how to use his hands. He caught me on the chin with a right that laid me out against some ties.

175

He was gone when I got up. And I went inside and began to bathe my face, and Tuck came in.

"Who whipped you?" he said.

"Oh, Alabama and I had a little argument," I said.

"What about?" he said.

"It don't matter, does it?" I said.

And then I saw that Mallory was standing there watching us.

"It might matter a lot," Mallory said, almost in a whisper. "Do you want me to ask him?"

"No," I said. "I don't think it's necessary."

"By any chance, it wasn't about playin' cards, was it?" he said. "I been hearin' some things said."

I wished that I had not mentioned Alabama's name. But it was too late to protect him. And Tuck said, "I saw you walkin' down the tracks with him."

"So we had a difference of opinion," I said. "I shouldn't have hit him. Just don't play cards with him."

Mallory kind of grunted and said, "It just happens that tomorrow is payday, a good day for him to go back to Elko." He turned away, and then paused and looked at me. "Don't worry," he said. "It was Tuck who spotted him first, the way he was playin' with the boys."

Tuck nodded, and said, "Yeah, I already told Mallory he should be watched. I don't like crooked gamblers."

Mallory nodded and went away.

And Tuck said, "Well, that takes care of Mr. Alabama. Poor guy, he can't never be vice-president of this outfit."

But I didn't feel like laughing. My jaw hurt.

And there were those summer evenings when Tuck and I would sit on a pile of ties along the right-of-way, which cut a smooth clean swath through the desert and ran off into the stars. And we would talk about what we would do when we owned the telephone company.

At night, the Limiteds roared by, east and west, pounding on the rails in a fine satisfying rhythm, and you marveled at the beautiful oiled machinery of the engines, never missing a beat. And the Limiteds made you think of the places they were going, and of which of them you knew, and you held mind pictures of Salt Lake City and Denver and Reno and San Francisco.

"You'll never get to be vice-president of this outfit, neither," Tuck said. "First time it gets hot you think of Montana and Glacier Park. Then when it's cold, you talk about 'Frisco and the ocean and the green hills and the big trees and how blue the Pacific is. I should tell the company about you, so when you pull out suddenly some day, it won't be such a shock to them. They won't be counting too much on you taking it over soon."

And this night Mallory shook me out of bed and told me to get dressed. The aisle between the bunks was filled with men swearing and grunting, getting into their clothes.

"We got to go out," Mallory said in a hoarse tone. "The line's down somewhere between here and Section Nine."

Rain rattled against the dead black windows. I drove Mallory's pickup ahead of the big truck. The water cut in the sides, and we bent toward the windshield trying to protect our faces. And the lightning cut golden canyons ahead, flashing magnificent photographs of the mountains and making them look bigger than ever before. In the truck the men huddled under a canvas. At times the headlights seemed to be stopped by a solid wall of darkness, and I tried to drive by feeling the ruts against the wheels.

The poles were slick, and your hands grew stiff with wet cold on the wires. You slipped and dangled. But the belts held. And you thanked God for honest workmen somewhere, the men who had made them.

"Double-time you're getting for this," Mallory said.

177

"Contact!" a man called out of the blackness.

"Contact!" another said.

George was the last down from the pole on which the break had occurred. He came over to the truck laughing, a hand bleeding a little. And he and Tuck got in a wrestling match.

"They say it takes hell to fight hell," Mallory said.

The snows had spread on the Ruby Mountains, and the ground was brittle, and the mornings made you swing your arms to get your blood stirring with warmth, and the water in the tank car began to freeze, and when the wind blew the old coaches were like iceboxes, and you had to stay near a stove to keep the chill out of your bones.

And this day in early October we went into Elko. We were given tickets to Portland. But I got to thinking again about San Francisco and the sunshine on the coast ranges, and the bay and the ferries with the gulls following them.

I had been a lineman long enough. I never wanted to see another telephone pole.

And I returned my ticket and quit.

The San Francisco Limited left Elko at midnight. I had an hour to wait when I took my suitcase and walked over to the depot. I went into the lunchroom and idled with a cup of coffee.

I felt that another chapter in my life was being closed, and I wondered what would happen to me.

And then a hand touched my arm. It was Doris. And she also had a suitcase.

She ordered some toast and milk and red jello.

"Well, well," she said. "We meet in the strangest places."

"Going away?" I said.

"Just ask me," she said, "and I'll tell you about this country and all the people in it."

"I'm asking," I said.

"Did you hear about it?" she said.

"About what?" I said.

"The deal," she said.

"Collapsed?" I said.

"Like a fart in a gale," she said. "I'd never laid eyes on this cowhunky of hers, had I? None of us knew him. How was I to know what he looked like?"

"I guess you couldn't," I said, "if you had never seen him."

"Because he gets tight and comes in, was I to ask what his name was?" she said. "Was I to know by looking at him that he was her big cow-and-acre man?"

"What happened?" I said.

"She accused me of trying to beat her time, that's all that happened," she said.

"And you're out," I said.

"So is she," she said. "She nearly beat him to death before we got her off him. Now what do you think?"

She lit a cigarette. And I couldn't have told anything about her if I hadn't known who she was. She was wearing a dark blue serge suit and a little round blue hat, and a neat white blouse, and her shoes were patent leather, and she would would have looked in place in the lobby of the Palace Hotel.

She said quietly. "You look down, too. Are you broke?"

"What if I was?" I said.

She only sniffed without taking her cigarette from her lips, and she laid a twenty dollar bill on the counter.

"I don't want your money," I said, "but thanks, anyway."

"Ashamed of it?" she said.

"I didn't say that," I said. "I'm not broke."

"Is that your bag there?" she said.

"Yes," I said. "I'm waiting for the train."

She picked up her bill. "West?" she said.

"San Francisco," I said.

"Me, too," she said. "I'm going down there and get some

o' that Nob Hill money I always heard about. I've got a compartment, and you can have the upper if you want it."

The train whistled and we got up. I carried her bag out and set it on the platform. When the train had rolled to a stop, she said, "You don't want it, the berth? It's paid for."

A trainman with a lantern came up to us, and he said, "You folks for the Pullmans?"

"Yes," she said.

"Just her," I said.

"All aboard," he said.

She took up her bag, and a porter stepped forward to help her.

"Maybe I'll see you in San Francisco some day," I said.

"Why didn't you ever tell me about the letters?" she said, but there was no reproachfulness in her tone.

"He got them," I said.

And then I took my suitcase and hurried forward toward the day coach.

13

I T HAD BEEN ALMOST A YEAR since I had seen Leo Begay when I came upon him in the Santa Fe Plaza. He was sitting on a bench, his long legs stretched out before him, his dark handsome face impassive, and he gave the appearance of a disconsolate young Navajo whose outlook on life was anything but encouraging. However, I was aware of the fallacy in such an impression. We had worked together the previous summer on a cattle ranch in northern New Mexico, west of Raton, and we had become good friends. He was by nature cheerful and enthusiastic, but it was his way at times to look as if he were brooding over some dire personal tragedy. As it had turned out, that was not the case at all. The truth was, he was suffering from nothing more than acute nostalgia. Shortly before he had quit his job, he had confided in me, "This place is too far away. I go back to my people." His home was near Chilchinbitoh, southeast of Kayenta, more than three hundred miles distant by the most direct wagon tracks and trails. He had set off alone early one morning, a few supplies and a pan or two wrapped in some blankets tied behind his saddle, and he had not looked back before disappearing over a ridge west of the ranch. Often I had wondered about him.

When I stopped before him he gazed up slowly, his eyes brightened with pleasure and he gripped my hand and pulled me down on the bench.

"You made it home all right."

He nodded. "You work here now?"

I told him I was wrangling horses on a guest ranch just outside of town. "What are you doing in Santa Fe?"

A shy smile crossed his face. "I get married," he said in his soft husky voice. "She wants to see Santa Fe, so we spend all my money coming here on the train. We have not been on a train, neither each of us. Now she goes to see the pictures in the museum. My feet get tired, so much walking around."

We had talked for some time before I mentioned the artist. "It was in the paper the other day. No one has seen him or heard from him for more than two months. He's from Los Angeles, and his family is worried. I guess they're wealthy, because they have offered a reward to anyone who can find out what happened to him."

"How much?"

"I think the story said a thousand dollars."

"Much money . . . Where did he go?"

"They think up toward Navajo Mountain."

He was silent. I felt that he was gazing far beyond the Plaza, perhaps envisioning Navajo Mountain lifting its great deep blue bulk over the San Juan Country. Suddenly he looked intently at me. "You think of going to find him, maybe?"

"I had the thought."

"Very rough country. No good roads. Horses only."

"Do you know it?"

"I been there. Looking for the cattle and horses of my wife's father. He has many and they go far sometimes. Good grass in the high country." The expression of sorrow momentarily filled his eyes. "I have no money to buy the things. Now I go back to work for her father. All money spent. We go home broke."

"You have the horses."

He moved a hand, as if to indicate that problem was easily solved. "My wife comes now. Dona."

I glanced up. She could have been no more than sixteen or seventeen. She wore a full crimson skirt and purple velveteen blouse that revealed the slenderness of her shoulders. Her long dark hair was tightly pinned back by a silver clasp. A squashblossom silver and turquoise necklace cascaded from her brown throat. There was a smile in her lustrous eyes but her expression revealed nothing of her thoughts. We shook hands, and she sat down beside him, and he talked to her in Navajo.

"She sees many good pictures," he said to me, and gave a short laugh. "Now her feet are tired." Then I knew he told her about the lost artist, for he said, "She hears some talk once. She thinks he went through Kayenta. He was young man. Maybe twenty. That's all she hears. Maybe very hard to find out where he goes. She does not talk the much English, but Spanish, yes."

"I suppose it would be no use."

She spoke to him, and he said to me, "She thinks only maybe. She thinks nobody can go through Navajo Mountain country and not be seen. Somebody see him someplace, she say. I think so she is right, too."

"You mean that she wants to go?"

"She goes. She knows it better than me, even. Long time lived up there when she is little girl." He smiled at her, and then he said bluntly, "You have money?"

"I have two hundred dollars," I said.

He told her, and then said, "You spend for things we need. She gets the horses." They both laughed, and he told me, "We divide the thousand dollars, half to you."

I agreed, and I thought they both were as excited about the prospect of the adventure as I was. It was arranged that we would meet in Kayenta in a week. I walked with them to the auto stage which would take them to Lamy, where they would board a train for Gallup.

"*Adiós,*" she said and gave me a strong slender hand.

They both looked very serious as the stage moved away, but I knew they were very happy.

Summer rains had played havoc with the dirt and gravel roads. At Fort Defiance I had been fortunate to get a ride in an Indian agency car. The driver was a taciturn white man who seemed to harbor an intense dislike for both his work with the government and the magnificent country through which we were passing. When he learned the purpose of my journey, he snorted contemptuously. "Hell, if he went up in that Navajo Mountain country you nor nobody else will ever find him. They're a no-good bunch of Navies up around there, and they don't like strangers," he said in an ominous tone.

It had been his hope to drive straight through to Kayenta, but flash floods forced us to stop overnight at Lukachukai. The sun was low when we reached our destination the next afternoon, and I unloaded my saddle and bedroll in front of Wetherill's Trading Post. He drove away, presumably for the agency office, without saying good-by.

A thin, gray, rather bent man came out of a nearby building and said, "I'm Wetherill. Are you the one Leo Begay is expecting?" When I told him I was he motioned to me to go inside. "I'll send a boy for him. He and his wife are staying with some people two or three miles down here. The clerk will give you a room." He started away and stopped. "The last one, too. Bunch of tourists arrived a while ago," he said, as if he thought the information would interest me.

It was dusk when Leo came in and clapped me on the back. After we had eaten supper we went into my room, and we had been talking there for some time when Wetherill appeared in the door. He spoke to Leo in Navajo, and then said to me, "I asked him if he had told you what I had learned. He said he hasn't yet told you everything, and maybe I could do it better."

"He told me you have been making some inquiries," I said.

"Yes." He dropped down on the edge of the single bed. "You know a lot of people come through here now. We're crowded most of the time. A lot of artists, too. Somebody said I should be selling oil paints and canvas and such things, but I don't think it would pay. Most of them come well supplied." He paused and gazed at the floor. "My memory isn't as good as it once was, I guess, but, you know, I remember this fellow very clearly, although he stayed here only one night, and I didn't see very much of him. I had to look at the register to get his name . . . Roger Call . . . I'd forgotten it, but that's not strange. However, the reason I remembered him so clearly was not because of the way he looked. It was because of the way he acted. He was very strange, sort of far away, if you get me, and . . . ah, well, unfriendly. Several people, I learned later, tried to talk with him, but he seemed to want to avoid everybody. Frankly, I didn't like him the moment I saw him, but that's not important. All we ever knew around here was that he was going out toward Navajo Mountain . . . or so he said . . . to do some painting. He had two burros. One he was riding and the other he had loaded with packs. He left early in the morning and never said a word to anyone that I know of."

185

"Then it's not known which way he went," I said.

"Oh, yes, I found out which way he went, but that doesn't mean much. He took the trail toward Keet Seel, over beyond the wash. People saw him."

"Go many places that way?" Leo said.

Wetherill nodded. "Exactly. When this story about him disappearing came up . . . oh, that must have been more than a month after he had left here . . . I began to ask some questions. There were two old Navajos in here one day, and I asked them about it."

"Yazzi and Big Man," Leo said.

"Yes," said Wetherill. "They've been here a long time, all their lives, and if anybody would know what's going on around here, they would. They knew about the young man with two burros, although they didn't say they had seen him. But they knew the direction he went."

"That's all?" I asked.

"That's all," said Wetherill, "except old Yazzi said he went far. How far, he claimed not to know. Just far." He looked at the floor, as if he might be giving consideration to his next words. "As I told Leo, I had the feeling that old Yazzi wasn't telling me everything he knew." He stood up. "Nothing can be done about that, either, and I might be wrong. Sorry I can't be of more help." He paused in the doorway. "Strange thing, but none of the Navajos around here want to try to find him. A Navajo policeman was here the other day, and we talked about it. He was mystified because no one had tried to trail him. At least, he couldn't learn that anyone had been out looking."

I suggested that there must be a reason why they didn't want to become involved. Wetherill gave a slight nod.

"A white man, any white man young or old, is a damn fool to go up in that country alone, unless he knows it. You can get lost up there quicker than you can wink," he said and

186

When we had passed over the ridge we rode into silence.

grinned at Leo. "He and Dona know it all right. At least, they won't get lost. Good luck," he said, and went out.

We bought our supplies in Wetherill's store, and I let Leo and Dona select what they wished.

"She's good cook," Leo said. "Make good meal with sheep. We get it on the way."

"He eats too much," Dona said.

They had brought six horses with them, three equipped with packsaddles. It was nearly noon by the time we had loaded them. We ate lunch and then started. She led the way down a path that crossed the wash and then climbed a long ridge that broke against the blue sky. Dark rain clouds were gathering in the west, mounting in great thunderheads. When we had passed over the ridge we rode into silence. Suddenly the world of noise had vanished, and ahead as far as my eyes would reach tumbled a broken land of great mesas and canyon walls and tilted slopes.

Willie Hat joined us on the fifth day after we had left Kayenta. In that time we had passed perhaps two score widely scattered hogans. Leo and Dona had talked at length with the people living in some of them. We had encountered several bands of sheep, and they had spoken with the boys and girls herding them. All their inquiries were disappointing. Some of the Navajos questioned said they had *heard* that a white man with two burros had passed *nearby* in the early summer, but none of them would admit that they had seen him.

"Man with two burros not ghost," Leo said. Anger touched his voice. "He comes this way. We get to Dunn's Trading Post, maybe tomorrow or next day." Dona said something to him in Navajo, and the anger gave way to a laugh. "She say I eat too many peaches. Only one can left. We get more at Dunn's."

It was almost sunset when Willie Hat arrived. We were camped in a narrow canyon through which a trickle of water

191

ran among immense boulders. A great shoulder of Navajo Mountain was visible to the north, catching the last streamers of the sun. Across the canyon were the crumbled ruins of an ancient cliffhouse. We could see a horseman riding slowly toward us on the little animal trail that twisted along the canyon floor. He was still a quarter of a mile away when Dona spoke.

"She say he follow us all the afternoon," Leo said. "She see him twice, far back. I think I see him once. Not sure. She has very good eyes."

"Why?" I said.

He shrugged and made no reply.

The rider stopped and sat motionless looking at us. Then he moved a few feet closer. His eyes fastened on me in a penetrating gaze before turning to the fire over which Dona was roasting the ribs of a kid we had obtained from a herder in the morning. He spoke a few words.

Leo nodded. "He say smell good."

"Do you know him?" I said.

Again he nodded and motioned to the man to dismount. "Willie," he said, as if he were speaking both to me and greeting the visitor. Then he added, "Hat. He lives in Tsegi."

Willie Hat spoke to Dona, but she only glanced at him with cold eyes and said nothing. He and Leo talked as he unsaddled his horse. He was a young man, perhaps no more than twenty, and he moved with a slight limp. A round head perched between powerful shoulders. His face was broad and his cheeks full, as if with excessive fat, and thick lips drooped beneath a flat nose.

I saw Leo point to the small meadow a short distance up the canyon where we had hobbled our horses, and Willie Hat led his mount, a large bony bay, toward it. Dona spoke with obvious crossness without taking her eyes off the cooking food. Leo replied quietly, and then sat down beside me.

192

"She does not like him," he said.

"I suspected that," I said.

He nodded. "His father, Martin Hat, is good man, very many sheep. Maybe twenty thousand. Five thousand horses, maybe. Very rich. He not like his father."

"Willie Hat?"

He nodded. "Makes trouble. Brings whiskey in. Sells it. Then people are drunk and fight. No pay bills at post. He not work with his father. Do nothing. Get in trouble. Once he put in jail, but his father pay big fine and get him out. Kind man, and very disappointed. Willie Hat makes him trouble."

"He's an ugly one, all right," I said.

"More ugly inside," Leo said.

"Why is he up here following us?"

Willie Hat was approaching, and Leo said, "I am finding out."

I had the feeling while we were eating that Dona was studiously avoiding looking at any of us. Willie Hat and Leo engaged in an animated conversation. It was almost as if they they were speaking in the sign language, for frequently they gestured in ways that made me think they were describing country, drawing contours on air. I felt uncomfortable listening to them and not understanding a word they said. Dona washed our utensils in a pool, and restored them to a packsack. Dusk was falling. I gathered some sticks for the fire. When I returned she had disappeared.

I spread my bedroll and lay down. Stars were appearing above the canyon. Leo and Willie Hat had stopped talking. They were two shadowy hunched figures at the edge of the firelight. It was very still, and I felt relief when I heard a faint birdcall. Presently Willie Hat drew a blanket around him and stretched out. Leo got up and moved quietly away into the darkness.

193

I was almost asleep when I heard him speak. He sat down on the ground beside me.

"He say we passed where the artist went," he said quietly. Instantly I was fully awake. "Passed it? He found him?"

"No," Leo said.

I sought to suppress my excitement. "But where? How does he know?"

Leo's voice was quiet and calm. "Not far. Maybe six miles."

"Well, how does he know?"

Instead of answering my question, he said, "He hears that we are looking." It was as if he were insisting on repeating in proper chronological order what Willie Hat had told him. "Everybody knows we come now. It is told in Kayenta. Then it goes with people fast to other places. Soon everybody hears it. He comes out to find us."

"That doesn't sound quite true to me," I said. "How could he find us? We've gone through a hundred canyons and arroyos, over a hundred ridges, twisting and turning. I don't think anybody could follow us."

"Maybe hard . . . maybe more people watch than we know. They tell him. Maybe somebody else follow us and show him. Six horses leave fresh good trail. Maybe not so hard as you think."

"But that still doesn't . . ."

"I know," he said. "How does he know where artist went if he does not find him?"

"That's right."

"He found burros and place where artist camp. Not artist."

"What happened to him, to Roger Call?"

"He say artist gone."

"Oh, hell, gone where? Did he walk out on foot? Where is this place?"

194

"We passed early this morning."

"We passed it!"

"You remember the big red wall. You speak about it, how big and straight it is."

"Yes."

"Beyond is a big canyon, and we can see the ruin, the houses in the cliff. You speak about them. How old and you would like to get into it."

"I remember."

"That's near the place. Up the other way, to the west is very long canyon, maybe two, three, miles long. Very narrow. We did not go in it. Somebody built a log fence across mouth. I have been there. No other opening. That's why I do not look there. Anybody goes in it can come out only where the fence is."

"You mean it's a box canyon."

"Yes. Somebody use it for pasture to keep horses in. Maybe stolen. Or maybe sheep for a time. Build the fence to hold them." He got up.

"Do you believe him?" I said.

"Maybe . . . we go tomorrow to see," he said, and vanished into the night.

I knew a strange apprehension as I fell into a fitful sleep. Several times during the night I awakened and sat up. The fire had gone out and I could see nothing but the stars foaming overhead. Once I heard a horse snort, and I wondered if some animal might be prowling about. Leo had told me there were cougars in the Navajo Mountain country, and I wondered if I should get up and speak to him. Then my reasoning, undoubtedly influenced by weariness and a warm bed, told me that if the horses were in danger he and Dona would be aware of it. Besides, he had a rifle . . . just then a very consoling thought. After that I knew nothing more until morning. When I opened my eyes, the sun was touching in a steamer of gold on Navajo Mountain. As I sat up, I saw that Dona was busy at the fire, and Leo was saddling the horses. Willie Hat was not in sight.

When I approached the fire after washing in the little creek, Dona smiled, waved a hand in a motion that encompassed most of the world, and spoke.

"Good morning," I said in reply.

Leo came up behind me. "She not say good morning," he said with a grin. "She say Willie Hat gone. She hope far away."

"Why?"

"Who knows?" Leo said. "He not say. Just go. Very early in the light. I see him go. He not tell us good-by." She spoke again, and they both bent over with laughter. "She say Willie Hat a thief. He take the last can of peaches."

It was midmorning when we came to the log fence that had been constructed across the mouth of the box canyon. The gateway was made of light pine poles. We removed them and rode in. Perhaps half a mile ahead, under an overhanging wall, was the rubble of a prehistoric cliffhouse. Willows and cottonwoods along one side of the canyon indicated the presence of water. Leo rode slowly toward it.

"Good spring there," he said.

The two burros suddenly came in sight as we made a turn about some rocks that had broken from a cliff. Leo stopped and studied them.

"Fat now. Grass good in summer," he said. "In winter snow deep here. They starve to death."

"Why didn't Willie Hat turn them out?" I said, but he made no reply.

He turned his horse toward the cottonwood grove, and we followed him in silence.

The water from the spring formed little pools for some distance before it vanished into the earth.

"He camp there," Leo said quietly, and we dismounted. The remains of a small shelter tent that had collapsed lay under a large tree. Nearby a small wire grill was fixed with some flat rocks and beneath it were the blackened ashes of a cooking fire. Dona retrieved a frying pan from a clump of trees. Moving about we recovered a cup, two tin plates, a saucepan, a packsaddle and a leather packsack that had been gnawed by rodents.

Dona spoke and stood staring into a patch of sage. Leo went to her, and knelt down. When he stood up he held a small palette stained with various colors. A further search produced two brushes, one of which was broken.

"No paints," Leo said. "Everything scattered." He handed me the palette and walked slowly about the campsite. When he stopped, he said, "Somebody throw everything around. Take things away. No clothes. No bed. No food." He moved on.

I came upon a small pit in which there were several rusting tin cans and a broken catsup bottle. Apparently Roger Call had dug the pit as a depository for trash and had intended to cover it when he left the canyon.

Leo leaned against a tree, and his eyes reflected the question in his mind. Dona was gazing up at the ruin as she spoke to him.

"She say maybe he tried to get up there," he told me, and shook his head. "Nobody could get up there."

I mentioned the possibility of an accident, a fall in which Roger Call broke a leg or his back, and died before anyone found him.

"Maybe," he said.

"Do you think we ought to look for a grave?" I said.

"Couldn't find," he said. "Canyon very long. Many rocks. Grass and weeds and other things grow. Wind blows dust. Rains wash dirt. Many rains up here. Take a very long time and many people to look." He spoke to Dona, and she turned toward the horses. "Search all through," he said.

"You believe he's dead," I said.

He stared at me in a way that suggested he thought I should realize the sad truth of things. "He's dead," he said.

We drove the burros out the gate, and left it open. Then we started back for Kayenta.

A Navajo policeman and a white deputy sheriff came to talk with us at Wetherill's. They said men would be sent to verify our discovery, Willie Hat would be questioned, and Roger Call's family in Los Angeles would receive a report. I had the thought that whatever the report said, it would never satisfy them unless a body had been found and identified, but I decided the subject was irrelevant.

I said good-by to them in front of the trading post.

"She say you come to see us sometime," Leo said.

"That I will," I said. I watched them until they were out of sight. Neither of them had looked back.

I never saw them again.

Forty years later my wife—Donna with two n's—and I drove south from Mexican Hat through the incomparable magnificence of Monument Valley on a paved highway. Some buildings of the Wetherill Trading Post were still standing, forlornly reflecting their age. They were occupied by a Navajo store and café. Only a few yards away stood a modern motel.

After registering I chatted with the clerk. I mentioned how many years had passed since I had been to Kayenta, and I told him briefly about the search for the lost artist, whose name I had forgotten.

"Well, that's very interesting," he said amiably. "I expect it looks a little different now, all these government buildings and so on." He laughed. "Not to mention the motel."

198

Shortly afterward someone knocked at our room. I opened the door to find the clerk and a small, graying woman with very bright blue eyes standing there.

"I hope you don't mind," he said. "This is Mrs. Grebb, the proprietress. I thought she would like to hear what you told me."

"Come in," I said, and introduced Donna to them.

"I must get back to the office," the clerk said, and left.

"Please sit down," Donna said to her.

"Thank you." Her eyes, almost the color of turquoise, held to my face as she dropped into an easy chair. "Ed said you told him something about looking for a lost artist."

"Oh, long ago," I said, and I told her about the search, and about finding the camp. "Of course, we didn't find out what happened to him, really, and I never heard anything more about it . . . in all this time. Were you here then?"

"Not right here," she said. "I grew up not far away. My father ran a post over near Dennehotso. I knew about him. His name was Call."

"Well, I wonder if . . . " I began, but she interrupted me.

"Everybody knows what happened to him," she said as if casually remarking about the pleasant weather. "He was murdered."

"By whom?" I said as calmly as I could.

"By a Navajo," she said. "By a drunk. Every time he got liquored up he bragged about how he had killed him. He wanted him to paint his picture, and when the young fellow refused they got in a fight, and he hit him in the head with a rock."

"Then they found his grave?"

She shook her head. "He never said what he did with him or where he buried him."

"Was he convicted?"

She gazed curiously at me, a smile touching the corners of her lips. "He wasn't even charged or tried. What could the police do? You can't try a drunk man, and when he was sober, he denied everything and said he knew nothing about it. The police thought they had him once. He tried to sell a set of oil paints at our store." She shrugged. "All he would say was that he found them somewhere in the brush when he was drunk. They held him three days, until he was sober, but they couldn't get anything else out of him. Circumstantial evidence, I think the police said." I had the impression she was looking clear through me. "You and your Navajo friends found a palette and some paintbrushes, didn't you?"

I walked across the room. "Did he admit that he met us, Leo Begay and Dona and me?"

The smile spread from her lips across her face. "I was waiting for you to ask that. He didn't deny meeting you, but he claimed he didn't go with you to the place where you found the things."

"That's true," I said.

"You know who I'm talking about now, don't you?"

"Yes," I said.

"They did get him once afterward for selling whiskey, and sent him to jail for ninety days, but it didn't cure him. He just went on getting drunk and talking . . . and then saying he didn't remember a thing he had said. After a while nobody paid any attention to him."

"Where is he now?" I said.

"In his grave," she said. "About five years ago he got drunk one winter night and fell off his horse and froze to death."

She got up. "Well, it was nice meeting you."

14

I T WASN'T EASY to get to Toh Chin Lin, and there were times when I wished that I had never heard of the place. Yet, there were compensations, memories I would treasure, although they always would be somewhat clouded by bitterness that I would not be able to overcome.

The sun was hardly more than man high on that fresh May morning when we drove out of the Shiprock Agency, heading west. The man at the wheel of the greatly overloaded pickup was Benjamin Franklin Yazzi, a Navajo whose extraordinary physical strength was made apparent by a glance at his broad shoulders and heavy arms. Although he was not as tall as I, standing three or four inches under my height of six feet, sitting beside him I was somewhat unpleasantly conscious of my own frailty.

A red corduroy shirt and blue jeans, faded with washings, seemed to be stretched to their limits over Ben Yazzi's thick body, which I had no doubt was as hard and solid as its appearance suggested. When he would push his wide hat to the back of his head, which he did frequently when he talked, as if the gesture made it easier for him to express himself, an unruly shock of hair would fall over one side of a broad forehead. His eyes were two black discs set in strongly sculptured red sandstone. They were almost devoid of expression, steady in their gaze, until he smiled or laughed. Then a glow would appear in their depths, as if reflective of the amusement some thought gave to him.

I had met him only the evening before we started, but the agent at Shiprock, a balding, round man named Gordon Markham, had told me something about him. "You'll find him very intelligent and reliable," Markham said. "He's one of the best interpreters I ever knew, and I've been in the Indian Service nearly twenty years. I really hate to have him go away from here all summer, because I need him." He shrugged. "The way of things . . . but the boss at Defiance said to send him, so that's it."

"He doesn't seem to have any accent," I said.

Markham had a way of not looking directly at you when he talked, as if his eyes were focused on something beyond you and he were thinking about something else rather than about what he was saying. "I guess he picked up English faster than most kids at the mission school," he said. "Anyway, if he had an accent he lost it in the Army. He spent eight years in the infantry. Came out of the war a sergeant, but he doesn't want to be called that. He smacked a smart aleck we got here one day for saying 'Yes, sir, sergeant', derisively, you know."

"No back talk," I said.

"That's right," he said. "I guess his experiences made him sort of . . . ah, serious-minded. Wounded at the battle of Chateau-Thierry, 1918, I think, in France. But there's nothing mean about him, nothing mean."

The gravel road curved and dipped and climbed through

the immense ashen and umber and yellow sweeps that reach away to the sky west of Shiprock. We had been driving perhaps half an hour, talking very little, when Ben Yazzi looked at me with a smile and said quietly, "Why did you take this job?"

"I thought it would be interesting," I said. "I like the Navajo Country and I like the Navajo people." That was the truth, but not all of the truth. I seemed to sense that he wasn't quite satisfied with my reply, and I said, "Besides, I needed a job."

He nodded, as if that statement were more acceptable. "The trucks load in Shiprock today and start tomorrow," he said. "The tents and cots and blankets came from Fort Wingate yesterday. Army surplus, I guess. The mess equipment, too. Big stoves."

"Yes, Markham told me," I said. "I have the job of taking an inventory when we get them. All the tools and other equipment, too."

"How'd you hear about the job?" he said.

"A friend of mine in Gallup, with the agency. Fort Defiance asked him to find somebody," I said. I thought it might be undiplomatic to disclose that my friend had told me, "You're just the kind they're looking for. They want somebody that can keep accurate accounts, order supplies, handle a payroll . . . all that sort of stuff. You've worked around a lot on ranches, and you understand how they must be run. These things don't take care of themselves, and the Indian Service is particular as hell about accounting for things these days. Learned a sad lesson long ago. They're afraid to let a Navajo handle it. Anyway, there wouldn't be very many who could . . . not way up in that remote place, especially. The white clerks in the service wouldn't do. Hell, in the first place they wouldn't want to be shunted off way up there for all summer, and in the second place you get most of them away from a desk and they're lost souls."

I didn't tell him any of that, and how I knew it wasn't true. Benjamin Franklin Yazzi . . . they gave young boys names like that in mission schools . . . was fully competent to handle the whole thing himself.

"Are you an engineer?" he asked. "Do you know how to build roads?"

I laughed. "The answer is no to both questions. I was told there would be Navajos up there who would know."

His heavy lips twisted in a brief smile. "They know, like cattle know how to build an easy trail to water. You let them alone and they will find the best and easiest way."

"More instinct than anything else," I said.

"Maybe," he said. "They'll build it where they think it should go, but it's not needed."

"But the money, the wages, are," I said.

"That's right," he said. "They need a lot of things more than they need a road. They've had several hard years up there. Drought and then bad cold in the winter. The grass has been poor. Two dollars a day and board will look like a lot of money to a hundred men up in that country. Most of them are bad in debt to the traders."

"Then I'd say it's a worthwhile project," I said.

He seemed amused by some thought, and presently he said, "Inventory . . . you'll have to keep a close eye on the food supplies. They'll take them off to their families, if they get a chance."

A short distance beyond Beclabito the road swung northwest to get around the Carrizo Mountains, a great blue wall spreading in wings from Pastora Peak, which still had snow on it. And then we were in Arizona. We stopped near Teec Nos Pos, and opened a can of peaches and ate some canned meat and bread. Heavy dark clouds were gathering over the mountains, and Ben Yazzi gazed at them as he munched his lunch.

"Maybe we don't get there today," he said. "The washes might be running too much to get across."

A few miles east of Red Mesa we left the gravel. A small wooden sign said, *JEHOVAH MISSION.*

"We don't go that far," he said.

He seemed to be letting the pickup follow of its own accord the two ruts that snaked their way up a high ridge. From the summit I gazed over a vast tortured country of mesas and canyons. We were west of the mountains, in a wild tossing sea of scrub trees and sage. Water was running in Chenlini Wash, and he got out and stood looking at it for a few moments.

"We can make it," he said. "I think. Hang on."

He raced the engine and then let the pickup plunge forward. It hit bottom twice and nearly turned downstream, and I thought he had lost control, and we were drenched with spray, but he kept the accelerator down to the floor, and we pulled up on the opposite bank, He got out and looked underneath.

"Muffler broke," he said.

The ruts forked, and another little arrow sign pointed the way to the mission. We took the other branch, and the motor fell once more into rhythmic, if noisier, purring, obviously having sustained no injury in its ordeal. We climbed steadily, making hairpin turns, twisting almost constantly, following the rugged contours.

"I don't see how trucks can ever get through here," I said.

"They can if it's dry enough," he said. "Otherwise we'll have to get wagons. The people around here have them. That's all they have. There ain't another pickup or car in this whole area."

"I haven't even seen a hogan," I said.

He smiled. "You don't know where to look. Lots of

people move up here in the summer. The grass is usually good up high for the sheep."

Then the forest began, great magnificent pines parading over the slopes, marching off into a sky that had cleared to turquoise. It was like an endless park with the sun streaming through the trees on meadows green with spring.

The ruts vanished at the edge of a wash, but I could see them resuming their way on the opposite side. He found a way through the stones on the wash floor, saying as he fought with the wheel, "This is very bad when it rains hard. We're lucky. Just a little wet."

A few minutes later he stopped the pickup at the edge of a level grassy park between walls of thick pines. "Fine big spring here," he said. "Over there. It runs all the time."

When the motor died the silence was broken only by the slight soughing of the trees.

"Beautiful place," I said, feeling as if I should muffle my voice to a whisper. "What do you call it?"

"Toh Chin Lin," he said, and gave a soft little laugh.

The trucks did get through, although they had to wait a day after unloading before starting back because the Toh Chin Lin Wash was running, ripping out banks and rolling stones along with a frightening roar. I marveled at the skill of the Navajo drivers. They seemed to know exactly where to turn out, which rocks to move, where the earth would hold and where it would give way.

"I didn't think it would be possible," I said.

"Sometimes that's difficult," Ben said.

"What?"

"The impossible," he said, and looked quickly behind him. I followed his gaze, and I saw a large group of men watching us from the edge of the trees. There must have been forty of them, and they were silent and motionless.

206

"The first come," Ben said quietly. Then suddenly he became the Army sergeant. In a strong commanding voice he spoke to them in Navajo. Later he told me what he had said, "All right, we got work waiting. Don't bring any horses in here. There's good grass out there. You know where it is." We had put a tent for my own quarters, and he had ordered them to line up before it. "Give your names to him, Johnny. He will put them in the book so you can get paid. Line up. Line up. Hosteen Largo first."

The man who stepped toward me moved with fluid grace and dignity. He was tall, slender, strikingly handsome, his eyes placid, darkly lustrous pools, the features of his apricot countenance almost delicately carved. He wore heavy shoes with thick soles, tan trousers and a loose purple velveteen shirt drawn in tightly by a wide belt adorned with silver conchos, and a necklace of turquoise and coral hung half way down to his waist. His hair, containing a sheen in its blackness, was long and held smoothly back by a round bun tied with white string.

"Hosteen Largo. The leader," Ben said, and spoke a few words in Navajo. "I told him he would be the camp foreman," he informed me in a way that made me understand I had no choice in the matter.

I shook his hand. It was thin and very strong. "Glad to meet you," I said. He only nodded.

"He gets three dollars a day," Ben said. "He knows all the men, and they respect him. He can counsel better than me or you." As if he read a question in my expression, he added, "It's all right. He speaks some English."

Hosteen Largo smiled, and said, "I pleased to work with you, you say so."

"I say so," I said.

Before the day was out the tents stood in a row with precision no Army camp could have surpassed. Ben made them move one when he found it to be several inches out of line. The mess was in operation, and three cooks, appointed by Hosteen, were busy at their stations preparing the evening meal. The rest of the men came in during the afternoon.

"Everybody will wash their own dishes," Ben said. "I will inspect them. They have to be clean. Everybody will make their own bed, and the blankets will be neat. I will inspect them every day. The garbage will be put in the cans, and it will be taken into the pit and covered with dirt."

And that evening they built a great fire, and a drum beat, and they sang, and some of them danced, and there was gay laughter and story telling. Sitting with me in front of my tent, Ben said, "You noticed that most of them are long hairs."

"Yes. Do many of them speak English?"

"No. Only a few. Hell, maybe some of them have never seen a railroad train," he said. "I bet most of them ain't been farther from this area than maybe Shiprock or Kayenta."

Then I saw Hosteen was approaching. He spoke with Ben in Navajo, and Ben said to me, "They want you to talk with them."

"Is something wrong?" I said.

Hosteen shook his head. "No."

"I'll translate for you," Ben said.

I got up. "I'm willing, but what do they want me to talk about?"

"President Coolidge and Babe Ruth," Hosteen said.

"Babe Ruth! How could they know about him . . . way up here?"

"The traders get papers," Ben said. "They tell them things."

"I'll do my best," I said as we started toward the fire. "It might be better, though, if I talked about something I know more about. Like American history."

208

"It don't matter," Ben said. "These men are anxious to learn."

"American history good. Navajo history bad," Hosteen said, and there was an inflection in his tone that I didn't like.

That afternoon I was working on my books, the interminable records required by the agency, when Ben came in and told me a woman had arrived and wanted to talk with me. I thought he was joking. "Pretty and young?" I said.

"No," he said. "The lady from the mission."

She was large and bony, and her feet were large and her hands were large, and she wore shoes that might have been G.I. issue, and a loose woolen skirt and a blouse that revealed the spareness of her shoulders, and her hair looked like an old gray mop perched on her head, and her eyes were green ice, but her smile was warm and her voice was modulated, and she had a distinct New England accent.

"How do you do," she said pleasantly. "I'm Mrs. Charity Hobson, the missionary here."

Her hand was coarse and hard and strong. "Come in," I said, and motioned Ben to join us in the tent. "I have only this one chair."

She sat down. "That's perfectly understandable, just getting things established. You selected a lovely place for your camp. I've come to make arrangements to hold services. Say three times a week. In the evening, of course, as I understand that the men will be out working during the day. Sunday, of course."

"The men are not here Sunday," Ben said. "They go home Saturday afternoon."

"Well, then, we'll have to make it three evenings," she said, as if the matter were settled.

"Just a minute," I said. "What do you have in mind?"

She became enthusiastic. "Why, you know I have a

portable organ. We'll bring it up and just leave it here for the summer. Paul will, that is. He's my assistant." She tittered. "I call him my right hand, sometimes."

I had seen Paul standing by her pickup. His hair was short and he wore a business suit that I suppose had been sent out with other old clothing to the mission, and I had the impression that he might not be certain of where he was or why he was there.

"I wish Hosteen was here," I said.

She bristled. "Hosteen Largo?"

"Yes," I said.

"Well, I don't see what he has to do with this," she said in a stiff tone. "You're in charge, aren't you?"

"Hosteen is the leader of the men," I said. "I like to get his advice."

She drew a deep breath. "Well, if you will pardon me, I don't think he is a very wise choice."

"We think he is," Ben said.

Anger touched her tone. "Hosteen Largo is a medicine man. He's . . . he's a heathen."

I had a little difficulty in suppressing a smile. "Well, that's neither here nor there. I'm sure you didn't come here to discuss Hosteen."

"Indeed, I did not," she said with what I thought was unnecessary firmness. "I would like to hold the first service tomorrow evening. Of course, you will order the men to gather at . . . say seven. That is, if it's not raining."

"Now, just a minute," I said. "Please let me make my position clear to you. I am the manager of this project, this camp, and I am responsible for what happens here. There my responsibility ends. I have no authority whatsoever to dictate what these men will do in their free time. As long as they obey the rules, that is all I ask of them, and it's all I have a right to ask. I have no right to intrude on their private lives. That's their own business."

She glared at me. "Do you mean that you refuse to allow me to hold services here, to lead them in prayer, and teach . . ."

I interrupted. "I did not say anything like that."

"Well, you are . . ." ▪ ᐧ

Again I interrupted her. "Please listen. You are welcome to bring your organ here, if you wish, but I have no right to tell these men that they must attend your service. It's not my business whether they sing or pray or listen to your sermons. All I said was that I will not order them to do it. Religion is not part of this prescribed program, and it shouldn't be."

She stood up. "Well, I think you are making a very serious mistake. What is your church?"

"That's rather personal, isn't it?" I said.

The green ice fastened on me. "I shall be here at six tomorrow evening." Her voice was haughty now. "The Lord help your conscience." She turned abruptly and went out.

Ben and I watched them drive away.

"That Paul is retarded," he said. "She feeds him and gives him clothes. The poor bastard. He follows her about like a lost dog."

"Is her husband a missionary, too?" I said.

"I wouldn't know," he said. "He's never been around here."

Mrs. Charity Hobson didn't get back the next day because the wash was running, making a roar like a freight train crossing a steel bridge. But she and Paul drove in promptly at six o'clock the following evening.

"I suppose it's all right if we put the organ out here where they have their fire," she said in a cold manner.

"Anywhere you like," I said. "I hope you have a cover for it."

"I have," she said, and motioned to Paul to drive the pickup down to the woodpile.

And as the evening settled I watched in utter fascination, almost in disbelief, the scene before me. A large rawboned woman sitting at a little organ, pumping life into it with her big feet, and singing in a throaty voice hymns I recognized but in words I could not understand. For she was singing "Oh, Come All Ye Faithful" and "Throw Out the Life Line" in Navajo. The fire crackled and spit out sparks, and its light caught on her face and revealed her ecstasy. She was in glory.

Only three men stood near the organ and they seemed to be staring at it, and paying no attention to her. All the others had disappeared beyond the reach of the firelight. The organ breathed its last note, and she stood up, and she lifted her arms to the stars.

"Come, let us pray," she called in a fervent voice. "Come, gather together before the Lord."

She waved her arms toward the trees, and she swept the universe with them, and she cried out again to the silent men to come to her. But no one came, and even the three men who had been intrigued by the organ music vanished as if they were shadows absorbed by the night. She stood silent for a few moments, her head bowed. Perhaps she was praying. Then she spoke to Paul, and he put a rubber poncho over the little organ. Together they walked slowly to the pickup and without speaking to anyone drove away.

Ben and I stood there watching the red taillight move its crooked way across the wash. "I feel sorry for both of them," I said, but he remained silent.

And then I heard the drum. It was throbbing softly. And I saw the men gathering about the fire. The rhythm changed, and the chanting began, rising and dying away and rising, in tones only the Navajo know how to give to the stars.

Two evenings later they were back again, and the same

weird scene was repeated. She told Paul to put the organ in the pickup, and then she stood staring at me in front of my tent.

"Sorry it didn't work out," I said. "They don't seem interested."

She appeared to be coldly calm. "You are a tool of the devil," she said. "You did this. You told them to stay away."

Before I could reply, Hosteen spoke. I hadn't seen him approach.

"No," he said. "Not him. Me."

She whirled on him. "Don't speak to me, you witch doctor. Both of you will answer to God in Heaven for this. Both of you are sinners, and the day of judgment will come for you," she said, and she spun about and got in the pickup.

I turned to speak to Hosteen, but he was moving away as silently as he had come, and I let him go.

I heard the motor one quiet afternoon when I was working at my table, and I went out to see who was coming. The little car was snaking its way across the wash, almost concealed from view at times by the great boulders. It moved by fits and starts, and I could see the driver's head protruding from the side of a windshield that was laced with cracks. The engine sounded as if it were having difficulty deciding whether to proceed or stop and rest. Later I would understand that was the way Dr. Andrew McDonald drove, riding the clutch, racing one moment and coasting the next. He came to a roaring, jerking, stop, and greeted me with a wave of the hand. The door stuck as he tried to open it, and he gave it a kick, and emerged.

"Noisy old thing, isn't it?" he said, offered his hand, and introduced himself. "Muffler's cracked a bit."

That wasn't the only affliction from which the old Chevy was suffering. All four of its fenders were wrinkled, its sides were dented, wads of packing bulged out of the upholstery.

"Welcome," I said. "I had a note that you would be visiting us. How can you see through that windshield?"

"It's not easy, especially if it's raining. The wiper's broke," he said. "I get along, though."

He stood scarcely six inches over five feet, and he was wrapped in wrinkled khaki, the pants tucked into laced boots, and he was bareheaded. His tousled hair glinted in the sunlight, resembling an assembly of attenuated coppery wires. Steel-rimmed glasses rode a pudgy nose under heavy eyebrows, and his large blue eyes seemed to be constantly gazing in wonder on the world about him.

"Where do I put my gear?" he said with a shy smile.

"I have an extra cot in my tent," I said.

He nodded. "Good enough," he said, and gazed toward the mess tent. "That would be the best place to set up shop, I guess. In the morning. When they get their chow. Some of them will probably be sick the next day."

"From what?" I said.

"The vaccinations." He squinted at me. "Didn't they tell you why I was coming?"

"No," I said. "The note I got said simply for examinations."

A peculiar smile twisted his lips. "There's been some trouble some places. Perhaps they thought it best not to give advance warning. Some of these people have a way of disappearing." He took a battered bag from the car. "I'm not popular every place."

Ben Yazzi knew Dr. McDonald well, and he told me something about him that evening. "He's the best doctor in the country," Ben said. "I guess he breaks every rule the Public Health Service has . . . if he wants to. He does what he pleases. He goes where he wants, or where he thinks he can help somebody. I seen him once sit with a squaw in a hogan for three days and three nights. She was having trouble having a baby, and she would have died if he hadn't done what he did."

"What did he do?"

"He . . . what do you call it?" Ben said. "He got a kettle of boiling water and boiled his tools and poured alcohol or something over them. He cut her open."

"Caesarian operation, I think," I said.

Ben only nodded.

"What happened?"

"He saved her and the baby," Ben said. "It was up in Monument Valley. They're still talking about it up there. Ain't no singer or midwife could have done that. The magic man, they call him. But not all of them like him."

"Why not?"

"He ain't always been successful," Ben said. "He operated on a man once with a ruptured appendix, and the man died. I can understand that he got there too late, and nobody probably could have saved him. But not everybody can understand. Anyway, he's the best doctor ever come to this country. Hell, he'd drive a hundred miles in that old rattletrap just to help a man with the shits, I think. These people may not realize it, but he's the best white man friend they got, if they could only understand." He moved his big hands in a gesture of hopelessness. "It's the older ones. They cling to the old ways. Singers. You can't change them."

Dr. McDonald was up with the sun. He took over a mess table and set up his paraphernalia. Ben followed my orders and told the cooks not to serve breakfast to any man until he had been vaccinated, and they obeyed. The first five men were ministered to without incident. Then the trouble began. The sixth man in line refused to bare his arm. Ben talked with him in Navajo, but he only shook his head.

Hosteen Largo stepped forward and spoke to me. "This man don't want it," he said.

215

"He has to," I said.

"No," Hosteen said. "If he do not like . . ."

Ben Yazzi was the sergeant once more. "Come on, you!" he said. "Open your shirt!"

"No," Hosteen said. "He do not want."

Ben whirled on him. "You get away from here."

Suddenly Dr. McDonald threw an arm around the neck of the unwilling patient. "Open your shirt," he said in Navajo. The man twisted but Dr. McDonald hung on to him. They fell to the ground, and the doctor went down beneath him. They rolled over.

"Help him, Ben," I said, and Ben sprang foward, pushed the doctor away and pinned the man to the ground, sitting on his chest, one hand at his throat while with the other he opened the man's sleeve. "Go ahead," he said to the doctor, and the doctor knelt down and performed the vaccination. Ben got up and stood glaring at the others in the line. "That's what will happen to anybody who gets smart," he shouted.

There was no more trouble. Even Hosteen submitted, although with obvious resentment.

And that afternoon I watched the little doctor drive away, his head protruding out the side of the windshield as he wound his way in the decrepit old car across the wash, the motor alternately dying and racing with new life, until at last its sounds were lost in the forest silence. He didn't say where he was going. And I never saw him again.

The two young men who came with the money looked very much alike, although they were not related. Both wore high-heeled boots, tightly fitting gabardine pants, leather jackets, and hats with wide brims. Their expressions were serious, and it seemed to be an effort for them to smile. I remember them only as Ed and Jack. Ed drove their pickup, which was equipped with camping gear, and his eyes and hair were dark. Jack was his superior, and his eyes were coldly blue, his hair a sand color, and he carried a large automatic in a hip holster.

They had not been there long before two white traders drove in. I never knew how they heard that it was payday at the camp, but I suppose they must have been told by the agency or by Ed and Jack. I had the payroll ready.

"We'll pay this evening after supper," Jack said. "Tell the men to line up outside your tent."

I didn't like the way he took charge, but I followed his instructions. I put a kerosene lantern on my work table. They brought in three heavy leather sacks. The men would be paid in silver, dollars and half-dollars. Jack and Ed piled the shiny coins on the table, and Jack sat down behind it, while Ed sat at one end with the payroll. The white traders wanted to come in the tent, so they could see how much each man was paid, and could collect from those who were in debt to them, but Jack told them to stay outside. They stood in front of the tent beside their car with their account books on the hood. They kept the car lights on so they could read their ledgers.

Ben and I sat on cots as the dispensing of the money proceeded. Ed called out the names, and the men came in, one by one, got their wages, put their thumb print on the payroll sheet, and went out. The task was almost half completed when another car drove up and came to a sudden stop. A man burst into the tent. He was a big Navajo, a short hair, and his face was dark with anger.

"You don't tell me," he said in a tone of fury.

"He's a trader down here," Ben said to me. "Beatien Begay."

"You stay outside," Jack told him.

"You not tell me it is payday," he said in a rising voice. "You tell them, not me. These men owe me on credit."

217

"It's not our business to tell you or anybody else," Jack said. He spoke quietly, his eyes half-closed and fastened on the trader. "Go outside with the other traders."

Beatien Begay turned half about, as if he were going to obey. Then he leaped forward and kicked the table over. The dollars and half-dollars showered about the earthen floor.

"You not pay no more," he shouted. "I get my money before you pay more."

Jack had fallen backward when the table went over, but as he straightened up his gun was in his hand.

"Don't!" I yelled. "Don't use it!"

"Let him come," he said.

Beatien Begay moved slightly, as if he were going to attack Jack.

"Don't!" I yelled again, and I told Ben, "Get him."

Ben shot forward, threw his arms about the trader, and wrestled him toward the entrance of the tent.

Ed sprang to Ben's assistance, and between them they forced Beatien Begay outside.

"I'll kill the son-of-a-bitch if he comes back," Jack said.

"No," I pleaded. "They'll hold him."

"This is govermint money," Jack said, as if he were telling me something I didn't know. "I'm a federal officer. I'll kill . . ."

Ben reappeared. He had some blood on one cheek, but he said calmly, "He don't have a gun. He won't come back. They will hold him."

Then Ed came in, and we began to pick up the scattered money.

"There's going to be hell to pay if any of it is missing," Jack said in a tone of warning.

Ben spoke firmly to him. "None will be missing."

"Better not be," Jack said. He told Ed, "You go ahead

Jack had fallen backward when the table went over, but as he straightened up his gun was in his hand.

alone." And he moved to a corner of the tent, and kept a hand on the gun. "Start calling the rest."

When the last man had been paid Jack said to me, "You tell them traders to get out of here, out of this camp, right now. And you tell that Begay I'll kill him if he don't go quietly."

"Tell them yourself," I said. "You're running this show."

He stared at me a moment and then went out. When he came back he said, "We start back for Shiprock right now. You're coming with us."

"Why should I go?" I said. "The trouble's over."

"It better be," he said. "We've got to make a report. I'm going to report that son-of-a-bitch, and I want you as a witness."

"I suppose that's required," I said. "Who told the white traders?"

"It don't matter who told anybody anything," he said, and he glared menacingly at me. "I want you to back me up with the super."

"I don't approve of what Begay did," I said, "but I can see his point."

"These men don't pay him if he's not here," Ben said.

"Well, that's not my business," Jack said. "Get ready. We want to start."

The three of us were crowded into the seat of the pickup. Ed drove with skill, but with what I felt was unnecessary speed, along the wagon road, struggling to hold the car lights on the twisting ruts. Chinlini Wash was running, and we had to wait five hours before we could cross. We built a fire, but Jack moved away into the darkness, as if he were suspicious that we were being followed.

"He knows what he's doing," Ed said, "or he wouldn't have his job."

I dozed, and when I awoke Ed was cooking some bacon

over the fire and he had made coffee. It was midmorning when we stopped before the agency in Shiprock. When he was told by a secretary that we wished to see him on urgent business, Superintendent Markham asked us to come in at once. Jack told him what had happened, and motioned to me.

"He'll back me up," he said.

Markham didn't ask me any questions. "I'd like a written report," he told Jack. "You can dictate it to one of the girls, if you like."

"I can write," Jack said, and got up. He and Ed started out of the office.

"I suppose I had better go right back," I said. "Can I get transportation?"

"Ah, just a minute," Markham said. "I'd like to talk with you." He shuffled some papers on his desk, and studied one. Jack and Ed had closed the door behind them when he said, "There's something . . . I was going to send for you to come in. Sit down."

I waited, and I had the impression that he was gazing into far distance as he said, "I have a very disturbing inquiry from Fort Defiance. Really came from Washington to them, and they have passed it on to me to look into. It says . . . let me see . . . yes, it says that you refused to let the missionary, ah, Mrs. Hobson, hold services at the camp."

"That's not true," I said.

He cleared his throat. "It says that you and Hosteen Largo told the men to stay away from services, that you ordered them to stay away," he said. "I know Hosteen Largo well. Mrs. Hobson, too."

I struggled to keep my voice calm as I said, "That's ridiculous. Would you like to know exactly what happened?"

"Of course," he said.

I told him, and when I had finished he nodded several times.

"Of course, I don't doubt your word," he said, looking through the wall of his office. "But you know these situations are very, ah . . . awkward. These missionary people can make an awful fuss . . . about nothing, sometimes . . . and it looks bad on the record. You know, some dang senator or congressman takes it up, and . . . well, they're usually very troublesome, and no one is ever satisfied." He shuffled the papers again. "Perhaps it's just as well that you don't go back. Ben can carry on, I think."

"You mean that I'm fired?" I said.

He emitted a peculiar little laugh. "Well, I wouldn't put it that way, exactly. Not necessary at all. You understand I have to make a report. I have to deal with these church people. It sort of puts me on the spot, as I have to answer the inquiry."

"All right," I said, and I was no longer angry. I didn't care. "Can I have my pay, too? I'll promise not to kick over any tables."

Again the peculiar laugh came. "Of course," he said. "Of course. I'll state that you resigned. That will end the whole thing. The paymaster is just down the hall. I'll instruct him to pay you. Ah . . . very nice to have known you. Personally, I feel you have done your job well, but that's neither here nor there, is it?"

"No," I said, and went out.

15

THERE WAS THE SPRING when I knew an irresistible urge to write a novel. I was feverish with inspiration. Indeed. I had been writing it for weeks in my thoughts, building its structure and giving flesh and character to the people I would portray. And I held visions of myself enjoying a trip around the world, paid for by the royalties I would receive. I was convinced the book would be purchased by the movies and a great picture would be made from it.

"There goes Johnny Terrell, who wrote *The Little Dark Man*," people in Hollywood would say.

Santa Fe was the place to do it, I decided. It provided the right atmosphere. I would have the company of other writers and artists, as well as a charming and attractive environment.

I went there, and for ten dollars a month I rented part of a Mexican house in Canyon Road.

My quarters had only two rooms. They contained nothing

but some shelves and a wood stove, but they were large rooms, and they were freshly whitewashed. If the plumbing was sparse, it was easily available, and I found it adequate. My rear door opened onto a courtyard in which there was a pump which I shared with my landlord, Gonzalo Oviedo, and his family. The part of the house in which the Oviedos lived stood on two sides of the patio. On the fourth side was the backhouse, also a community enterprise. It was clean, painted a brilliant green, and always well supplied with papers of various types and colors, which I presumed Gonzalo obtained from the trash bins of the well-to-do people on Camino del Monte Sol whose gardens he tended.

In no time I came to know that the name of Gonzalo's wife was Isabella, that his youngest daughter, who was fourteen, was Magdalena, and that his eldest daughter had reached the mature age of sixteen and was named Carmencita. We all crossed paths frequently and unavoidably as we pursued our respective missions in the patio.

The problem of furniture was easily solved. I had six months' wages in my wallet, money which I had saved while working on a cattle ranch near Flagstaff, and when I had written home about my plan to engage in literary work, my father had . . . with voluntary generosity . . . sent me three hundred dollars. Both he and my mother not only had enthusiastically applauded my proposal but had expressed the conviction that I could not fail.

I bought a secondhand bed and mattress, a table, a chair, a kerosene lamp, an assortment of utensils, and rented an old typewriter. Carmencita displayed considerable interest in making me comfortable. She supplied a curtain for the small window that looked out on the patio, and she brought me a small worn rug to place beside my bed. A brush with a long handle was kept beside the backhouse, and she graciously in-

226

formed me that I was welcome to use it whenever my floor needed sweeping.

These acts of hers I looked upon as no more than neighborly gestures. But as days passed, and she had on several occasions appeared with dishes of frijoles, tamales and tortillas, I began to suspect that her thoughts regarding me were not entirely confined to my welfare. Strong doubts were raised, however, when I saw her going off to dances and other affairs with a young man whose name I came to know was Panfilo. He was a handsome gay young chap who walked with a bounce. There seemed to be no question that she was very much attached to him.

In a way, I was both right and wrong. I found that out one evening when she tapped lightly on my door. She had brought me a bowl of fine black cherries, and she explained that her father had picked them, with the permission of the owner of the tree, and that they were the first to ripen that year.

We sat on the edge of my bed eating the cherries. When I put my arm around her she made no resistance.

I left the door unlatched after that, and frequently she slipped in quietly, sometimes late at night, to spend an hour or so in bed with me, on each occasion vanishing into the dark patio as noiselessly as she had come.

When one evening I asked her about her intentions toward Panfilo, she shrugged her shoulders and tossed her head in a way that suggested defiance. "He wants to marry with me," she said. "I don't be in a hurry."

In the evening, in the light of my kerosene lamp, her skin was an apricot color, and it smelled a little like cinnamon toast, and her long hair was silky black, and her large dark eyes had lights in them. She had round firm breasts and wide strong hips.

It was, all-in-all, a pleasant congenial place . . . I worked diligently on my book . . . and I did not mention Panfilo to her a second time.

It was Magdalena who knocked with unusual vigor on my door early one morning. With her was a small old man with a deeply wrinkled sunburned face and very bright blue eyes.

"He brings good fresh eggs to sell," she said.

That was how I came to know George Slant.

After that he appeared on this day and that with his basket of eggs. We would sit for a time on a bench by my door, and that was the way I came to know a good deal about him and his life.

I am sure that I learned many things that few, if any, people in Santa Fe knew. We became good friends . . . the very old man and the very young man . . . and he would stop to chat for a bit even when he knew I did not need eggs.

It was this way:

You walked along a reach of yellow road that ran eastward from the edge of town into a purple break in the pinon hills to the old adobe house in which he lived. And you would think that the walls of that house, as bronze and cracked as his face, could have been no older than he.

You walked along this road in the afternoon, and the Sangre de Cristo Mountains stood up before you in a great emerald wall with golden tints lighting the high points and blue shadows lying in the canyons. The sun hung over a cloud of lavender mist, which was the Jemez Range, and usually they were swept at this time of day by the great blue brooms of rainstorms. The Jemez was the western wall of the valley of the Rio Grande, the river that ran from the sky through a land changing constantly its shades and tints. Southward was a colored patchwork of desert hills running down to the distant peaks of the Sandia, under an immaculate turquoise sky.

Suddenly you came upon his house. There it was, just around a sharp turn in the little road where tall sage hid the view ahead. To the left of it was a row of poplars, and there was a path leading through them to a round-pole corral and a dilapidated log barn with a dirt roof.

When George Slant lived there, and when his wife, Sally, was alive, there were tall hollyhocks, red and blue and ochre, standing in a wavering shaggy line across the front of the house. Strings of chili peppers hung in the sun from protruding eaves. A washtub sat on a box under the trees. In a high wire enclosure, built to keep out prowling animals, Rhode Island Reds and Leghorns scratched and dusted themselves in holes in the powdered earth.

Later on, people in Santa Fe who knew him and who bought his eggs and frying chickens, would speak of the place as "the cake house." I heard one or two of them . . . I'm sure they thought they were very clever . . . call him "the original cake-eater." Later, when I understood the gist of it, I thought it was a poor pun in my estimation, and it made me a little sick each time I heard it.

Both George and Sally had been born in the Middle West, but they migrated to the Southwest as young persons . . . although not together . . . and their bodies seemed to have adopted the ruggedness and dryness of the sunburned ranges. Their eyes seemed constantly fixed on distance, the infinite spaces of empty valleys under an empty sky. Their natures were as quiet, as calm, as the hills and mountains around them, and as unchangeable, although during the latter years of his life, he sometimes acted a bit childish. When I came to know him well I understood that he lived more in years gone than in the day at hand.

He had been born in the little town of Urbana, in Ohio.

229

It happened that I had been there, for it was also my mother's birthplace, and I had gone with her there twice to visit her cousins. This was a coincidence that excited him. I suppose it made him feel closer to me in some way, and more anxious to talk with me, even though it was apparent that our respective relatives had never known each other.

His father and mother had died when he was very young, and he had been adopted by a neighboring family named Gubbins. As soon as he was old enough to drive horses, he was put to work. He received no schooling, no training of any sort, except slaps across the mouth from a worn wretch poorly playing the role of his own departed mother.

There were two other children in the Gubbins family . . . a boy and a girl. They went to school, at least part of the year, and their ability to letter and write figures made it possible for them to ridicule their adopted brother for his ignorance.

Gubbins was a drunkard. He owned two teams of horses, and conducted a draying business. George worked on the delivery wagon, driving the horses and delivering the goods to customers while Gubbins dozed on the seat in a drunken stupor. At times, when Gubbins was too far gone to work in safety, George would go alone with the wagon.

When business was slack, as it was much of the time, George and Gubbins would drive to a hitching post on the square, where customers needing their service could easily find them, and Gubbins would go into a saloon, leaving George to wait for business.

It happened one day that George delivered some things to the little cottage at the edge of Urbana in which Myra Slant lived. Her husband had died some years earlier, and her only son, Bert, was a cavalryman in the West who came home on furlough once a year.

It was a cold winter day, and when George went into

Myra Slant's kitchen, she set out a cup of coffee for him and a plate of cakes.

He sat by the warm range as he ate. He had never tasted cakes as good as those she gave him. They melted in his mouth, and the taste of each bite seemed to linger. When he left, she gave him half a dozen wrapped in a small piece of cloth.

It was that visit to the Widow Slant's kitchen, and the eating of those cakes, which not only marked the beginning of their friendship but a turning point in his life. It did not happen, however, as quickly as that sentence suggests. His mind was dull. If he suspected that the world proffered many advantages and contained many wonders, he could imagine them only through the haze of his ignorance, if he could imagine them at all. He had never been beyond the limits of Urbana. So he had no real understanding that beyond the fields which surrounded the town the earth continued, flesh lived and died, the sun and moon and the stars shone, the wind blew, and summer followed winter.

But after he met the Widow Slant, he came to know that wonders did exist. Not the wonders of earthly life in distant spheres, not the wonders of nature. He came to know wonders far more simple. They were the wonders of common kindness, good food, and comfort, things he had never known in the fourteen years of his existence.

The Widow Slant was pleased to find someone, even a youth, who so greatly appreciated her cakes. She enjoyed making them. George in his rags, who ate them greedily and whose blue eyes spoke so plainly the thankfulness he could not express in words, awakened in her a great pity.

George became a regular caller at the Widow Slant's cottage, and always awaiting him was a yellow crock of cakes on the kitchen table. And there was coffee and milk. While he ate, she would tell him of her son Bert, and about some of his adventures as a cavalryman.

231

She would say: "Bert will be home one day soon. It's almost time. Then you'll see a fine soldier. You'll like Bert, and he'll like you. I know. You look a little like he used to, when he was your age, only his hair was darker."

And she would say: "My sakes alive, Georgie, you must wash your neck and ears. Here now, bend over while I take off some of that dirt."

And she would say: "Georgie, you need that hole fixed in your shirt. Take it off and let me patch it."

One day, she dug into an old trunk and brought out a pair of Bert's boyhood pants for him. Her eyes grew a bit misty as she watched him get into them.

On another day she gave him a pair of mittens she had knitted. But the Gubbins boy took them away from him. When he told the Widow Slant what had happened, her eyes flashed with anger, and she said, "I've a good notion to go right over there and . . ." then she grew calm and she smiled. "Never mind, Georgie," she said. "Let the shanty Irish have them. I'll make you another pair. God always punishes people like that."

When George was sixteen, Gubbins made what he called a "change in the work." He told George, "You're big enough to handle things alone all the time now. If you get anything to haul that's too big for you, get that nigger from Mason's store to help you. But you take care o' the money. And don't you be loafin' around none, just because I ain't there to watch you."

The "change" gave George a freedom that he fully appreciated. He stopped in the Widow Slant's house almost every day. By this time, he had met Bert Slant twice, and he thought him the greatest man he had ever known.

When Bert was home on furlough, George would go to sit in the Widow Slant's kitchen in the evening and listen to him talk about the West. Perhaps there would be two or three other men there who had known Bert as a boy. On such occasions the Widow Slant seemed to be particularly happy. She always had things to eat on the table, such things as nut bread and pie and a yellow crock of cakes. And everyone would munch and drink coffee, or if it was the summer and hot there would be a big pitcher of lemonade. It seemed to George that when Bert was home, his mother seemed to look younger, and she bustled about with a firm step. And in his simple mind he came to understand the love one person may hold for another. For the first time in his life he understood a thing that had always been mysterious to him, something he had wondered about, but had never experienced. Now he was experiencing it. But not only as it was portrayed in Myra Slant and Bert. He was experiencing it in his own feelings, his own love, for her.

"It's so nice to have him home, Georgie, but each time he goes back is more painful than the others," she said. "It's so hard to think that I might not see him again."

When she spoke like that, George's heart would thump wildly. He would have cried, because of his helplessness in the face of her anguish, if he had not come to know very early in life that crying was a waste of time.

A few times some of Bert's old friends brought their wives to see him. On those evenings Bert seemed to delight in telling Indian stories that made the women shudder and close their eyes, as if to shut out the terrible pictures his quiet flow of words painted. But George never shut his eyes. Those were the stories he most enjoyed, and he seldom took his eyes off the great cavalryman from the West with the immense bony brown hands, parched red face, and broad shoulders covered in the blue uniform tunic . . . the uniform that became to George a symbol of a land and of a life almost beyond the scope of his imagination.

Bert would say: "That was the hardest ride I ever had

233

folks. Two days through white alkali dust. And when we got
there, what did we find? Bodies, that's all. Bodies with their
eyes picked out by birds. Women and children, too. Not a
heart beating. Blood everywhere. Bodies left to rot in the sun
after they was scalped. It took us two days to bury them.
I tell you, folks, them Sioux is bad."

In the spring that George was seventeen, Bert came home
in a lieutenant's uniform. While he was there Myra Slant
died.

That evening, the boy and the soldier sat beside her
body in her tiny bedroom . . . the soldier who many times
in his life had been close to death, and the boy who knew little
of it, who had difficulty understanding the finality of it.

They sat in silence, until the soldier said, "She'll be
cremated. It was her wish. And she wanted her ashes scattered
out in a field. I won't put her in a grave. I'll do like she
wanted."

The boy's chest was full of pain and his throat was
choked. He would have liked to cry out a word, any word,
that might have brought consolation, but he said nothing, and
finally he went out, leaving the soldier sitting alone in the
dark room.

Soon afterward the boy and the soldier were walking on
a road beyond the town, between fields sprouting with the
bright green of spring. Bert carried a small urn.

Death and cremation and eternity . . . George Slant
had come to comprehend their meaning.

"By the creek over there," Bert said. "I think that is a
place she would like."

When they reached the creek, they sat down beneath an
old elm tree. Above them new and tender leaves trembled
with awakened life. The silence was profound, broken only by
a distant bird song.

Bert held the urn tightly clasped in his hand. His face

234

was strained, reflecting the emotion seething in him. Suddenly he closed his eyes, and he said, "I can't do it! By God, I can't! I don't want to see them."

He stood up and held out the urn to the terrified George. "You do it for me," he said in a commanding tone. "Take them up on the knoll and scatter them out where there will be a wind. Go now, and be sure to scatter them all. Throw the urn away."

Halfway up the knoll, George stopped and looked back. Bert was watching him and waved a hand in a signal to him to go on. And he went on to the top of the knoll, and the breeze was cool on his face.

He closed his eyes, and his hands trembled, as he removed the cap of the urn. He felt as if his hair was creeping on his head . . . then quickly he turned the urn upside down, and something soft struck him in the face, in his eyes and his mouth. He was so terrified that he dropped the urn and fell to his knees. Instinctively he rubbed his eyes. Something ground in his teeth. He spit and spluttered. It might have been soft clay, but there was no taste of clay. There was for a brief moment the taste of cakes.

He staggered to his feet and ran down the knoll.

Not long after Bert had gone back to the West, George left Urbana. It had become a place of desolation to him. Tears would fill his eyes whenever he passed her cottage. His life was more empty, more lonely, more difficult than it had been even in the dreary days of his childhood.

He ran away. And he took with him what money he could collect from customers and the few dollars he filched from Gubbins' pants while the sot slept. He had made up his mind to become a soldier, and he set out for Fort Russell, in Wyoming, where Bert had been stationed.

Bert had been transferred, and he never saw him again. But he became a soldier under the name of George Slant, a trooper in the cavalry. And he had served for more than a dozen years, in Wyoming, in Montana, and finally in New Mexico.

It was not long after he had been discharged from the Army and had become a freighter, hauling supplies from the new Santa Fe Railroad to inland settlements and ranches, that he met Sally.

It happened in Las Vegas, New Mexico, where he frequently went with his six-team, a warm June night with the stars wheeling overhead like a silvery mist, and he was walking along a narrow street, on the way to the rooming house in which he was staying. He had been gambling, and having won a bit he had bought several drinks for himself and his friends, so that he felt in fine feather. He was thinking that it was a night for adventure, a night for riding . . . but the old West was gone, gone forever. Better than Army life now was the life of a freighter, driving a six-team over desert and mountain trails to country that still remained undisturbed by the invasion of civilization. Life in the Army now was mostly waiting for something to happen, something one knew very well would never happen. Life as a freighter meant freedom, one could move about as one wished, without consideration for rule and regulation. Better the life of a freighter . . . but he would never forget the sound of the troop riding at night an empty range that reached away to the stars, the clink of bit and the clank of saber, the soft creak of oily leather, and the dull pounding of the horses' hooves on the dry earth.

That night as he was walking in the narrow street in Las Vegas he heard the shattering of a window. Something very nearly struck him in the head. The object landed in the street. He jumped into the protection of a wall and drew a revolver. Then he heard a woman scream. Perceiving that no

When George Slant was an old man he would sit down on the bench in my patio and talk of bygone days.

one was attacking him, he stepped out from the wall. Sounds of a struggle came from the house before him.

He rapped hard on the door with his gun, and then he kicked open the door. A woman was lying on the floor beside a table. There was no one else in the room, but a rear door stood wide open. Several chairs were overturned, and a bowl lay shattered on the hearth. It had been a similar crockery bowl that had been thrown through the window and had nearly struck him in the head.

He closed both doors. Then he lifted the woman to a chair and bathed her face with water. When she appeared to have got full control of herself, he sat down across the table from her, and as he could think of no appropriate words to speak, he remained silent. Once or twice she glanced at him. She was a slender woman, and her hair had a slight tinge of rust color in it, and her eyes were large and soft and very brown. At least she seemed to gather enough courage to look steadily at him, and she said, "Thank you."

"Will he come back?" he said.

She shook her head. "Not tonight." Then she stood up, still a little unsteady, and held to the table, and she said, "Damn him! No, he won't come back. He'll get drunk. He's a coward." She sat down again, and she trembled. "That's the last time he beats me," she said, in the way of taking an oath. "I ain't a-goin' to stand it no longer. I'm a-goin' off, I am."

There were the remains of a meal on the table. George's eyes had become attracted to a yellow dish. In it were four small cakes. Suddenly he reached out and took one. He held it up, as if contemplating its possible taste, considering its size and shape and color, as an artist might study a landscape before beginning to paint it. Then he stuffed it into his mouth. When he had swallowed it, he at once ate another. He ate all four, chewing them slowly and seeming to see nothing.

She had been gazing at him, and she said, "You must be hungry. I could warm some coffee and frijoles."

"I'm not hungry," he said, "but I'll eat another cake, if you got one. And a dipper of water."

She brought more cakes, which she took from a clay jar on a shelf, and set them with a cup of water before him.

"It's been many a year since I tasted cakes like them," he said. "I was a boy back in Ohio. Who made them?"

"I did," she said. "They ain't as good as sometimes, but then a person don't get decent flour here. Not like the flour we had back home in Illinois. Pshaw, I could turn out cakes then."

He seemed to be lost in profound thought. Suddenly he stood up.

"You want to get out of here?" he said. "You want to run off from him? Then you come with me. I'll be good to you. I'll take you to live in Santa Fe."

She was staring at him in complete amazement, and she slumped on the chair when she said, "How can I do that? I'm married to him. How can I go with you like that?"

He was excited. He said, "Who'll know? Who'll ever know? There ain't nobody in Santa Fe will ever know. He won't find you. Look, you said he was a coward. I know that. He run off when I hit on the door."

She was staring at him again, staring steadily at his face, as if she were searching for some sign, some expression, some false movement of a muscle, that would warn her not to consider his proposal. But suddenly she stood up, still staring at him.

"All right, Mister, I'll go," she said. "I don't even know your name, but whatever it is, it's mine now. I'll go."

When George Slant was an old man, and going about Santa Fe with his eggs, and shaking a snowy head in appreciation of the money he received from his few customers, he

240

would sit down on the bench in my patio and he would talk of bygone days, chuckling in a childish manner and blinking eyes which for all their years of unceasing service were as blue as the New Mexico sky.

Sometimes he would reach into his pocket and draw out a small cake. And he would munch it with toothless gums as we talked.

When he had emptied his basket of eggs he would trudge the reach of yellow road that ran eastward from the edge of town into a purple break in the piñon hills, go back to the old adobe house in which he and Sally had lived so many years, since they had run away from her husband.

One day when he was scheduled to come with his eggs he failed to appear. I recall that Isabella was provoked, and she came to borrow some from me, but I had none. She sent her youngest daughter, Magdalena, scurrying off to find him. That was how we learned that Sally had died.

A neighbor had found him sitting beside her body, lying stiff and white in their bed, and had summoned the police. When the undertaker took Sally away, George demanded that she be cremated, and he produced the money to pay for it.

One afternoon he trudged alone the little road out to the old adobe house. In his withered hands he carried a metal urn containing her ashes.

We who bought his eggs after that knew a feeble old man who had lost his childish chuckle, and who mumbled a good deal to himself.

I had completed my novel . . . I would have to rewrite it several times before it was published . . . and I was thinking of leaving Santa Fe. I felt the urge once more to move on. Moreover, things were not as congenial as they had been in the establishment of Gonzalo Oviedo.

Carmencita stopped coming to see me, and she frankly

announced that she was pregnant and had decided to marry Panfilo.

"He good man and works hard," she said. "Maybe I would have marry you, but you are crazy with sitting writing all the time, and no work, and you don't have no money. You talk about going away to all kinds of crazy places. He's got a good job in the same work with my father."

I never knew by whom she had become pregnant, but I fervently hoped that the honors would go to Panfilo.

And then a day or two before I left Santa Fe, she appeared at my door and stared at me with tragic eyes.

"He's dead," she said. "The old man with the eggs."

"When?" I said.

"Two days, maybe three, ago," she said. "They find him lying in the door of his house."

I had planned to see him before I left. Now I hurried out to the old adobe, scolding myself for not having gone sooner, and hoping I might be able to attend his funeral.

When I walked in, I found three men, all with very solemn faces, standing about a table. One of them asked me what business I had there. I told him that I was a good friend who had just heard of George's death.

Then he told me what had happened.

The coroner had thought it necessary, because of certain circumstances which he did not describe, to perform an autopsy and to have some chemical analyses conducted.

The chemist was one of the men standing beside the table, and he said, "Death was caused by poisoning, but I have not been able to accurately determine as yet the kind of poison. However, it seemed to be contained in some kind of cake he had eaten."

The coroner reached out quickly and took up a small cake from a plate which contained several. He broke it open. Inside it was a dull gray color.

"Well, here are your cakes," he said. "They couldn't have been made very long ago. See, they're still soft. He must have made them. He was living here all alone."

"I'll analyse them," the chemist said.

At that instant the coroner gave a start. He reached down and picked up a metal urn from the floor.

The top had been removed from the urn. And it was empty.

"My God," he said.

16

KNOWLEDGE AND UNDERSTANDING of western history
bring more pain than pleasure.

You can spend years in pleasant wanderings, knowing
a sublime freedom, in the West, as I had done before the age
of twenty-five. You can marvel at the West's wonders. And
you can be deeply moved by its bigness and its beauty and the
majesty of its canyons and the grandeur of its mountains
and the colors of its deserts and the perfumed sweeps of its
forests.

You can live and work in every western state, learning
something of the peoples and the ranches and the towns and
the ways of life and the characters of each of them. But if you
are addicted to the narcotic of looking backward, your enjoy-
ment of these years and your appreciation of what you have
seen and learned and accomplished are darkened by an in-
escapable shadow. And sometimes your memories and your
thoughts are infiltrated by distressful admixtures which spoil
them.

For example, you can admire the beauty of the old California Missions, but you know that those wrinkled serene walls belonged to the first organized penal system to be established in territory that would become part of the United States. You hold a haunting vision of the prisoners of those maleficent colonies, the Indians who were the slaves, whose civil and moral rights were denied them by the fanatical overseers, the *padres,* who lashed them for infractions, who pursued them with military posses if they attempted to regain their freedom, who threw them into cells, and starved them, and tortured them, and hanged them . . . all in the name of God.

You enjoy the smoothness and the comfort of the passenger trains . . . even the efficiency of the freights, if you bummed about on them, as I did. But you know that the western railroads were built by swindle, and by the theft of public money, and by the cheating and robbing of investors, and by the unscrupulous and unwarranted gifts of millions of acres of federal lands.

You know that the western railroads were allowed to deceive prospective settlers with dishonest advertisements and crooked promotions, to charge exorbitant and discriminatory rates. And you know that they escaped prosecution for their bribery of senators and representatives and governors and cabinet officials, and that judges in their pay absolved them of their crimes.

You respect the intelligence and the fine character of Indians you come to know in schools and on their reservation farms and far out in the deserts and plains with their flocks and their herds. And you know that the inhumane treatment consciously inflicted upon these people by both the American government and American society remains unsurpassed in the annals of any civilized power which, since the beginning of recorded history, has conquered a weaker and less advanced segment of mankind.

246

You know that it was the white Americans, not the Indians, who caused the wars between the two races. And you know that on the part of the whites they were wars of immoral appropriation and illegal confiscation, wars nurtured on political corruption, social depravity, economic rapacity and religious humbug.

You can be stirred by the sight of the ruts of the old trails west, the last fragments of them still defying the onslaughts of time and the elements to mark the course of continental empire. You hear the pioneers who penetrated the western wilderness extolled as heroes, one and all. And you know that is a fatuity. You hear them praised as courageous men and women who conquered the country against overwhelming odds, who fearlessly defied the savages and the beasts. And you know that is a falsity. You see heroic statues and murals of the emigrants. And you know they are ridiculous in concept.

You know that all the colorful euphemisms applied to the settlers are pap. For you know that the great dream they held was not of building an empire, not a dream of extending the Nation from ocean to ocean, but a dream of free land and free gold, a dream of getting rich with a minimum of exertion, a dream of getting something for nothing.

And you know that the early white peoples of the West were, with notably few exceptions, uncouth and common and crude. You know that they were the white trash of the East and the South and the Middle West.

You know that instead of bearing noble ambitions, instead of harboring burning desires to contribute to a greater America . . . as the hypocritical professional patriots and the maudlin politicians so greatly enjoy proclaiming . . . they were motivated by instincts generally attributed to wolves.

You hear tributes to the daring and bravery and suffering of the 'Forty-niners. And you know that these qualities and circumstances were the products of their greed. You attend

247

celebrations commemorating the Gold Rush Days, fêtes held in ghost towns with amusing homely names. You hear eulogies of men who struck it rich after great sacrifices, and retired to live in luxury in mansions in San Francisco. And you hear ludicrous stories of their antics and sad tales of their failures.

But you never hear that many, if not the majority, of them were men without moral scruple or conscience, a large number of them wanted criminals. And you never hear that these vaunted fortune hunters murdered thousands of Indians, most of these victims peaceful, backward and helpless people, in the promised land of California.

The bandits and the outlaws and the gunfighters and the renegades are venerated in innumerable books, and given eternal life in innumerable museums. And you know that they should long have been interred in a graveyard set aside for social degenerates, for diseased minds and depraved hearts.

Yet, while truly great men and truly good men are forgotten, the stories of these psychopaths are fed to the young of each succeeding generation with the intimation that there is to be found some virtue and honor in their immorality and in their injustices and in their deceit and in their crimes.

You read histories that are supplied to young students, allegedly to supplement their knowledge and education. And you know that they contain half-truths, misinformation and misinterpretations, and that they omit material that leaves pictures incomplete, and that some of them are unqualifiedly false.

The men whom romanticists like to call "cattle barons" provide a strong case in support of the aphorism at the beginning of this chapter. However, I cite it not only for that reason but also because I knew the West before the open range was entirely gone. I saw it when regional roundups still existed, when cook wagons were drawn by horses over hills and plains where there were no roads, when riders spent weeks drifting beef herds to railroad shipping points, and before the last vestiges of the old way of life had vanished.

The era of the "cattle barons" had ended—but only a few years earlier—when I worked on cow outfits in Montana and Wyoming and Colorado and the Southwest. Actually their reigns had been of comparatively short duration, beginning after the Civil War and ending in the first few years of this century.

The annals of the American economy contain no record of a commercial activity that was defended as legitimate business but which was more illegitimate than the raising of cattle on the public domain in this short period.

The "cattle barons" held their domains not by legal right but by force of arms and criminal violence, and through political corruption. They paid few taxes, owned little real property, and gave no thought to civic responsibility. They fought every proposal for the development and improvement of the West that was introduced in both Congress and state legislatures, opposed every program to bolster the general economy, and if they lacked strength in numbers they remedied this weakness with coercion, bribery and even murder.

The riders who worked for them never existed as they are pictured in the novel, the motion picture and the TV drama. The cowboys of the early days were common laborers, the serfs and mercenaries who carried out the commands, legal or illegal, of the suzerains employing them. Most of them were ignorant and ill-mannered, and all of them were poorly paid. So it will continue to be, with maudlin, inane, puerile horse operas and romances pouring from film factories and cheap publishing houses. For fantasy and folklore survive where reality and history are interred, and there is no preventative, no cure, for bad taste and stupidity.

You hear the bugle calls of the western cavalry proclaiming noble deeds and morally justified achievements. But you

249

know that they proclaim with the same clear notes base actions, fiendish massacres, and infamous triumphs.

You hear it said in book and drama that the pioneers were proud of their heritage. But you know that they could take little just pride in what they did with it.

I lift my glass in a toast to the Old West.

"May it never return."

Author's Note

SOME OF THE INCIDENTS in this collection of papers were used as the basis for fiction which I wrote nearly half a century ago for some small magazines. Although it is true that each of these publications was interred in a literary grave soon after printing one of my stories, I disclaim all responsibility for their respective deaths. Among them were *The Midland* of Ames, Iowa, *The Frontier* of Missoula, Montana, *The Prairie Schooner* of Lincoln, Nebraska, and *The North American Review*. To them I am grateful. R.I.P.